NGOSS Distilled:

The Essential Guide to Next Generation Telecoms Management

John P. Reilly
Martin J. Creaner

NGOSS Distilled
by John P. Reilly and Martin J. Creaner

Published by The Lean Corporation.

Typeset by Schiraz Limited.

Printed and bound in Great Britain by Cambridge University Press.

First Printing: September 2005

British Library Cataloguing-in-Publication-Data
A CIP catalogue record for this book is available from the British Library.

ISBN 0-9551087-0-5
ISBN 13 : 978-0-9551087-0-9

Table of Contents

Chapter Three

Chapter Four

Chapter Five

Chapter Six

Appendix

Table of Figures

Chapter One

Chapter Two

Chapter Three

Chapter Four

Chapter Five

Chapter Six

Acknowledgements

Books are never merely the work of the authors. The encouragement, support, and contributions of others are essential.

Thanks from John P. Reilly to my wife, Jeannie, who put up with me while I took time away from us to put this book together. Martin Creaner, who kept me focused when I tended to veer off into the bushes. Gary Nolte, of MetaSolv, who persevered by reading and editing the entire book. To a couple of my industry pals, Dave Raymer and Gabriela Chirbau, who guided me along the way. To Kim Klieger and Sriram Cheruvu, both of MetaSolv, who were with me from the beginning to the end of this endeavor. And, to John Strassner, my SID-team co-chair, who provided the inspiration to get started.

Thanks from Martin J. Creaner firstly to all the people who have made NGOSS a reality over the past four years. It is through their dedication, often above and beyond the call of duty, that NGOSS has progressed. Thanks to John Reilly for being my conscience over the past six months, ensuring this book made it to the shelves. A big thank you to Keith Willetts and Aileen Smith for their drive in getting this book in a fit state to publish. I'd also like to thank all the people who have provided valuable review comments on the drafts of the book. The book is infinitely more valuable due to your efforts. In particular Greg Fidler who devoted enormous amounts of his personal time to reviewing the book. Many thanks to the TeleManagement Forum for giving permission to reproduce some of their NGOSS content in this book. Finally I would like to thank my wife Carmel and my family for their patience in supporting me through yet another 'project'.

Foreword

When I started my career in the telecom industry, open copper wire was still used for the final 'drop' to a house. Call switching was performed by 'step-by-step' electromechanical Strowger switches in heavy steel racks. Orders were processed by a clerk writing the order on a pad of 10 colored sheets separated by carbon paper which was then sent by post to all of the relevant departments involved in providing the service. Billing was undertaken by guys with cameras that photographed mechanical meters and sent the photographs for processing by armies of clerks who worked out the bill by calculating the difference between the records and the latest meter reading.

When was this – the 1930's in some far-off land? No, it was the early 1970's in the British Post Office – an arm of government with a minister in charge. Customers were called subscribers (that is if they were lucky enough to get service), employees were civil servants who were required to sign the Official Secrets Act and the social culture was to make very short phone calls because rates were exorbitant.

The transformation from that world to today in a little over 30 years is truly outstanding. The business processes used then were almost totally manual and phone companies were usually the largest employer in any country. When computing did make an entry into the industry, it was for repetitive 'batch processing' tasks like bill production. Computers were used to support human processes – hence the name Operational Support Systems (OSS) that grew up to describe them and differentiate them from Business Support Systems (BSS) that originally handled things like payroll processing and so forth. Computing grew in the telecom industry on a piecemeal, department-by-department and ad hoc basis.

As the number of services grew and equipment became ever more sophisticated, the number of computers deployed within the network grew with them – often numbered in thousands of different types of support system based on virtually every type operating system, database, data structure and communications approach.

Many of these systems were developed in-house by people from various labs or IT departments. Most were written to support a specific process, for a specific operator running a specific service. And if these systems were inordinately hard to change and it took forever to introduce new services – well – no real problem! - where else were customers going to go? – it's a monopoly or something close to it!

While a few systems architects and dreamers may have foreseen the need for automating processes end-end, the economics of the telecom industry were so buoyant that few, if any, senior executives in operators saw the need for a unified and comprehensive re-think of how they ran their business. And so, while a commercial revolution was taking place on the surface of the industry, while the mobile industry was being born and growing up, while operators were introducing digital technologies and advanced services and while competition was re-shaping the marketplace, most of those OSS and BSS systems were quietly humming away in their fragmented, inefficient and ineffective way.

As the new century unfolded, there was a profound reckoning as we experienced the deepest ever recession in the telecom industry. Stock market values plummeted, balance sheets were laid waste and some half a million people in the industry lost their jobs. Finally the economic realities began to dawn that you could not survive in a 21st century marketplace by running with a 20th century operating model.

Some of us dreamers finally got enough backing from the industry to be able to lay out a blueprint of what a 21st century operator would look like and what kind of business processes and systems would be required to compete in brutal markets of falling prices, increasing need for business agility and ever improving customer service. That blueprint described a world where the systems ran the vast majority of business processes – the humans no longer undertaking repetitive and meaningless jobs but the rewarding ones of interacting with customers or inventing new and profitable services.

High levels of process automation, high levels of business flexibility, high levels of customer service and self-care coupled with ultra-low operating costs were the design vision for the 21st century 'lean' operator. To deliver that, a comprehensive systems and process framework was required to allow operators to plan their migration to a much more tightly integrated and automated method of operation. And so was born the New Generation Operations Systems and Software (NGOSS) program within the TeleManagement Forum. In fact it is an integrated set of frameworks covering business processes, information and data, systems integration and applications and is applicable to all systems used by an operator – OSS or BSS.

This book is a practical guidebook to New Generation OSS and its component parts. Literally hundreds of people from numerous countries around the world have contributed to the development of these frameworks, which are having a profound effect of the design and deployment of operational systems worldwide. Different aspects of these frameworks will interest different people for different reasons and the detailed specifications are easily available from the TeleManagement Forum. But now, for the first time, this book attempts to bring all of those threads together in a readable and understandable guidebook.

'NGOSS Distilled' is the first in a series of books being published that will make it easier to understand the 'big picture' as well as the practicalities of using these frameworks and tools. Written by two people who have been involved with the development of NGOSS throughout much of its history, I hope this book will give you a better insight into what NGOSS is and how to use it.

The telecom industry has transformed beyond all recognition in just a few decades and the rate of change is accelerating all the time. We can't imagine the services and technology we will have a decade from now, but we can imagine that there will still be demanding customers, shareholders will still want to see good profits and staff will want rewarding and interesting jobs. There is also no doubt that telecommunications will continue to have a profound effect on the daily lives and economic well-being of everyone on the planet. There is no going back to the days of monopoly, poor services and cripplingly high prices, so NGOSS has a hugely important role in enabling the telecom revolution to continue to unfold.

I wish you happy reading and hope you get a lot from this book.

KEITH WILLETTS SEPTEMBER 2005.

A Note from our Sponsor

When the pioneering thinkers first proposed NGOSS to the TeleManagement Forum, quizzical looks were the most common reply. After all, this was 1999 and the need to invest in a new wave of "back office" systems seemed like a waste when there were all these new fabulous network devices one could buy.

And then the party ended. The bubble burst, as did the valuations of many companies. Cost cutting became the watchword of an industry. Unable to compete on service, price wars became the norm and revenues (along with profits) took a dive. Suddenly, a more efficient way of operating didn't look so crazy.

As the sun began to shine again on telecom, competition heated up. But this time, customer service, quality and innovation became just as important as pinching pennies. With new players like Vonage, Google and eBay entering the market using VoIP, things suddenly look completely different than they did a few short years ago.

Today the question isn't "why do I need NGOSS?" It's "how do I implement NGOSS faster than the other guy?" That's why this book is so vital and why the TeleManagement Forum is proud to sponsor it.

'NGOSS Distilled' will enable everyone from senior executives to software developers to those on the front lines of operations to understand how NGOSS can work for them and how to put it into practice.

NGOSS acceptance and uptake is a global movement with operators on every continent using it or planning to. We hope this book goes a long way in helping them, their suppliers and their customers successfully navigate this transformation into the 21st Century of Communications.

Regards,

JIM WARNER
President – TeleManagement Forum

Chapter One
NGOSS and the Lean Operator

The telecom industry is very big business. With global revenues of over a trillion US dollars, it represents an appreciable percentage of the GDP of most countries. After decades of a feather-bedded life as protected monopolies in most countries, the past few years have seen a transformation of the market – an explosion of competition and new services. We've seen multi-billion dollar debt mountains, multi-billion dollar bankruptcies, multi-billion dollar mergers and acquisitions and even super-rich telecom CEO's headed for lengthy prison sentences. This is a world away from the 'regulated rate of return' industry that brought you black dial telephone service.

There are so many issues and pressures swirling around the telecom industry that it is possible to be too close and not be able to see the wood for the trees. But it is possible to try to boil down the issues to a few simple home truths.

First, the telecom industry and its markets have changed for ever.

The changes in the telecom market are irreversible and so a business strategy that relies on battening down the hatches and hoping for better weather isn't going to work. The only hope of survival and prosperity for shareholders is to go on the offensive, investing the right resources to get in shape to fight and win in the brutal marketplace that telecom services will continue to be. There is no storm to be weathered, this is the reality of life in a fast moving, highly competitive and innovative marketplace. New technologies are rolling in by the day, so are new demands from customers and new competitors are ready to strike. So change to a lean, agile and wily player prospering in this bear pit is not a one time change, it has to become a way of life – organizing and running the business to be capable of rapid change as markets and technologies change.

Second, you'll never make it with your old business structure, processes and systems.

While many telecom operators look reformed on the outside with their new names, logos and marketing, on the inside most of them rely on business processes and systems that pre-date the competitive marketplace. Many business processes are fragmented across multiple 'stove-pipe' departments and systems technology is even more fragmented across just about every type of operating system, database structure and user interface the world has ever invented.

That 'behind the scenes' picture means three key things:

• Those fragmented processes and systems significantly impair business agility – the ability of the business to adapt to change. You see this most clearly in the time it takes to launch new services or react to a competitor's move. You also see it in the lengthy order-cash cycles of many operators.

• Operating costs are inevitably higher with very inefficient processes and low levels of end-to-end process automation. With prices for most services in most parts of the world declining rapidly, the underlying cost base of operators is endangering profitability.

• Monopolies did not need to be customer friendly and often systems and processes are designed around the needs of the operator, not the customer. Add to that the cost reduction measures many operators have deployed (such as reducing manpower) and it adds up to generally declining customer service levels.

Of these three 'diseases' the lack of agility is probably the most difficult to overcome and the most dangerous for an operator. For decades they sold telephone lines, calls and leased circuits and pretty much that was it. The only differentiation between business and residential customers was which section of the phone book they were listed in and maybe some priority on maintenance. Nothing much changed year after year except maybe that push button phones made an appearance. That's the root of the business structure that's still in place in most fixed operators, the snail-like pace of change of the 20th century telecom market. And before we assume that mobile is different, where did all of the people and money come from to set up mobile operators in the 1990's? - from incumbent fixed line operators. And where did all of the talent come from to set up the second, third and fourth mobile operators - from the first mobile operator. So not until we saw the emergence of internet service providers did we see new blood with new ideas coming in to break the mould of 100 years of 'how things are done'.

Third, radical change demands radical change.

That the telecom industry is changing rapidly and radically is not in question. Mobile operators are introducing new information and video services on the back of new, high-speed network infrastructures. Fixed line operators are rolling out DSL quickly and will soon introduce similar services like video-on-demand. Markets are converging as everything becomes IP based and the first fixed-mobile converged services are likely to appear soon. The new entrants of the 1990's tended to look like scaled down versions of the incumbents and in the inevitable starving competition of the early 2000's, guess what – the fat man won. But the new competitors aren't weighed down by massive infrastructures to roll out and can move very quickly in areas like voice-over-IP services and focus on specific market niches.

The structure of the industry is changing fundamentally too, with the networking arms of infrastructure-based players becoming wholesale suppliers of transport services while competition moves more and more to service retailing. As services get richer with more content, competitors from the retail and entertainment sectors are bringing new approaches to the market meaning that the current crop of operators have to move even faster just to stay in the game.

Becoming a Lean Operator

The majority of operational problems stem from the underlying business processes, systems and data. These can be very deeply rooted – after all most operators have never radically overhauled the way they work. They've been through the introduction of subscriber dialing in the 1950's and 60's, through the introduction of digital switching in the 70's and 80's and the introduction of optical networking in the 1990's. Change to the way they operate has been piecemeal and departmentally based, never a thorough, systematic and radical overhaul for the 21st century. But just like many other industries before it, the telecom industry now faces this challenge if it is to survive and prosper. High operating costs, poor order-to-cash cycles, high levels of customer dissatisfaction driving high churn rates and long lead times for new products are not the hallmarks of a successful operator in a brutally competitive market.

The term 'lean operator'[1] is shorthand for an adaptive, fleet of foot enterprise who delivers excellent value to its customers and excellent returns to its shareholders. It does not mean an enterprise who temporarily increased profitability by simply squeezing costs at the expense of customer service because such an enterprise is unlikely to stay profitable for very long against competitors who offer better

---

1 The 'lean operator' approach applies not only to service providers, but equally to equipment vendors, system integrators, and independent software vendors.

services. The term 'lean' comes from manufacturing industry, specifically auto manufacturing and was pioneered by Toyota in the 1970's and 80's. The principles of lean manufacturing are widely adopted in manufacturing industries around the world and in recent decades have been adopted by service industries such as retailing, banking and airlines.

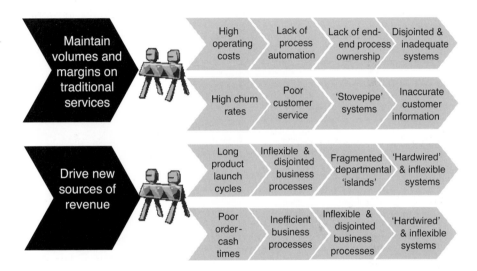

Figure 1.1 – Barriers to Becoming a Lean Operator

At the heart of a lean operator is a highly efficient business machine that focuses on improving the end-end process flow though the business - ever increasing the agility of the business, ever reducing the costs of operation and ever increasing the level of service delivered to customers. Greater and greater reliance is placed on the automation of those business processes with integrated and highly effective IT systems.

Reacting to these pressures and solving the operational problems and bottlenecks is the core of this book. Other books in this series will deal with the business and operational issues that weigh large in such a change, but this book is for those engineering and process executives and professionals charged with implementing the detail of this change.

Cornerstones of a Lean Operator

A lean operator is one that can react to change and bring its products to market faster and better than the competition. There are three cornerstones that underpin the capabilities of a lean operator and these are shown in Figure 1.2.

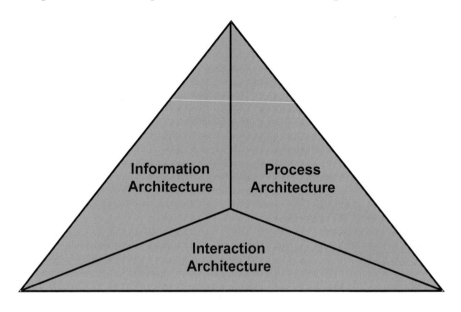

Figure 1.2 – Lean Operator Cornerstones

Information fuels a lean operator. An information architecture forms one of the three cornerstones upon which a lean operator thrives. An executive wants to know the uptake of a new product in the marketplace. Network engineers want to be able to quickly introduce new technologies into an enterprise's infrastructure. A customer service representative needs up-to-date information about a customer in order to respond to a customer's inquiries.

To respond to the executive's inquiry, information must be structured such that relationships between customer orders, products they buy, and market segments are easy to navigate. In response to the network engineer's desire to quickly introduce new technologies, the information must be modeled in such a way that new technologies can be introduced without the need to alter information structures. For the customer service representative, information structures must accommodate a large number of real-time updates.

Processes execute a lean operator's strategies and tactics to achieve the enterprise's objectives and goals. A process must be available for the executive to inquire about the uptake of a new product. The network engineer must have access to a process that enables the engineer to define new technologies for use in an enterprise's network infrastructure. The customer service representative must be able to use processes that manage the interaction with customers. A process architecture provides a structure that organizes and defines these processes and allows them to easily adapt to changes in an industry.

The interaction architecture brings together lean operator's information and process architectures. It defines formal interfaces (or contracts), which describe the details of a process's operation, the information required by the process and produced by the process, as well as technology-neutral and technology-specific architectures used to define and implement the processes and information.

The executive's market uptake inquiry process assembles information about products purchased by customers within market segments and presents it on a web-based dashboard. The network engineer uses a graphical display to define new resources and the services that consume the resources via resource and service definition processes. The customer service representative uses a generic customer interaction process that enables the representative to assemble varying facts, such as orders, service level agreements, and trouble tickets, about a customer's involvement with the enterprise.

Introducing the concept of "views"

Businesses deploy automation in the form of software applications, which manage the information and provide the interfaces to support the processes. The lean operator's approach to developing applications to support the business can be characterized through four primary views of the cornerstone architectures as shown in Figure 1.3. Each view exposes the aspects of the cornerstone architectures required to make decisions at various stages of the development lifecycle.

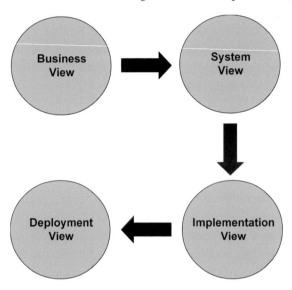

Figure 1.3 – Views of Lean Operator Cornerstones

Development progresses from one view to the next view. Each view has a different focus on a common set of artifacts that evolve from one view to the next.

Business View

The **business view** provides an implementation-independent view of the cornerstone architectures. Here the focus is on business processes, workflow, and associated information requirements. This view is built using techniques such as use case analysis.

There is no mention of application or technology implementation in the business view. There are no user interfaces specified, nor is there any mention made of where processes are performed or where applications will be executed.

System View

The **system view** is about "modeling the system solution". In this view the information model is expanded by adding additional details, such as operations to business entities. A 'grey box' perspective places the focus on points of interoperability and interactions between business processes, use cases, contracts and the information model. Process flows are further detailed to include system and information specifications. System view constraints, capabilities, and context are defined.

Implementation View

The **implementation view** brings the dimension of automation to the system view by specifying user interfaces and logic to support the business processes. To ensure that this view is adaptable, logic is separated into logical layers that have become commonplace in a well-designed distributed environment as shown in Figure 1.4.

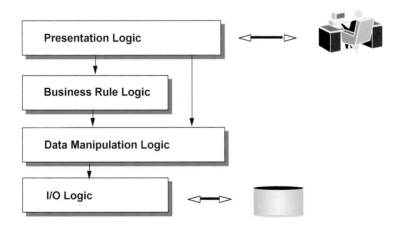

Figure 1.4 – Distributed Implementation View

The presentation layer supports only logic associated with the user interface. This includes logic such as moving from one user interface to another, handling system events, validating input, and formatting the fields on the user interface.

The business rule layer supports logic that applies business rules, such as calculating the interest amount for a loan. It may also call, or invoke, logic from the data management view, for example reading a table that contains interest rates and principal amounts.

The data manipulation logic layer handles all access to data, such as creating, retrieving, updating and deleting.

Layering logic in this manner, regardless of how it is packaged and deployed, minimizes the impact of change when it occurs. For example, if a Client/Server application initially employs a remote data style of implementation all the logic resides on the client machine. Suppose network performance reasons necessitate a change to a distributed process style. To do this you remove the data manipulation logic layer from the client and install it on the server. If the business rule logic layer employs any data manipulation logic you also remove it from the client and install it on the server. This involves much less work than having all of the logic mixed together on the client.

The fourth layer, the I/O logic layer, is optional. Whether it is included depends on the tools being used to develop the application. Some tools allow specification of the application's logic to be in terms of the attributes (or fields) of the user interface and not physical data structures. This layer maps the attributes to the physical data structures. I/O routines called by the data manipulation logic layer of the application's logic do this.

Including an I/O logic layer insulates each of the other logic layers from changes in the physical data structures and minimizes the impact of change. For example, suppose a database change moves the attribute, customer nearest relative, from one physical data structure to another. The I/O module that maps the attribute and performs the I/O is all that changes. The other layers of logic remain unchanged.

Deployment View

The **deployment view** provides the necessary hardware and software to support the application. This view represents the technical infrastructure that can cope with rapidly changing applications and user populations. Adding and subtracting capacity must be transparent. This is where a distributed computing environment is key. Employing tools that allow easy porting of an application from one physical environment to another without changing the underlying business, system, and implementation views is critical for the lean operator.

View Interaction

While each view can and does impact the others, they can each be analyzed and modeled independently. For example, use cases help structure the business view and system view by identifying business processes and objects that interact with the processes. These processes and objects then become the focus of an automated system constructed in the implementation view.

When change does occur you determine the impact on each view followed by the impact between the views. For example, suppose you want to begin accepting customer inquiries via the Internet. This definitely impacts the implementation and deployment views. You must investigate what type of equipment and software is necessary. Once accomplished, you can see how to adapt your current customer inquiry application to run on the Internet. Perhaps there is only a need for a new user interface that takes advantage of the Internet's capabilities.

The degree of impact between the views should be greatest as we move down through the views. A change in a business process, such as calculating an applicant's credit score, will undoubtedly necessitate a change in the implementation view if the score calculation is automatic. Moving an application from a mainframe to the Internet affects the implementation and deployment views. The impact of change as we move up through the views should be minimal for a truly lean operator. For example, migrating to a distributed processing environment will definitely change the implementation and deployment views. It will impact the implementation view (at a minimum to take advantage of a graphical user interface style), but should not impact the business or system views.

Introducing NGOSS at its Simplest

The remainder of this book is aimed at explaining NGOSS in various levels of detail and from various perspectives. However, it is appropriate here to give a very high level introduction to NGOSS for the reader who has not previously been exposed to the core components of NGOSS.

First and foremost, NGOSS is the TeleManagement Forum's (TM Forum) New Generation Operations Systems and Software initiative. It provides the technical framework that supports the lean operator as described above, giving enterprises the tools they need to undertake automation projects with confidence. NGOSS-based solutions use industry-accepted IT concepts and technologies to deliver a more productive development environment and efficient management infrastructure.

NGOSS, was first envisioned by the TM Forum in 2000 as a comprehensive, integrated framework for developing, procuring and deploying operational and business support systems and software. It is available as a toolkit of industry-agreed frameworks, specifications and guidelines that cover key business and technical areas. It is designed to deliver measurable improvements in development and software integration environments.

The elements of NGOSS fit together to provide an end-to-end framework for OSS/BSS development integration and operations, and elements of NGOSS may be used as an end-to-end framework, as part of a comprehensive methodology that is described in detail in later chapters, to undertake large-scale development and integration projects. Or the NGOSS elements may be used separately to deliver specific short-term benefits.

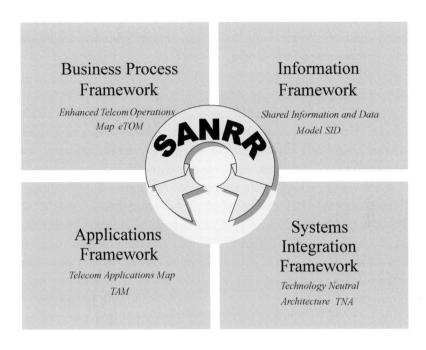

Business Process
Framework
*Enhanced Telcom Operations
Map eTOM*

Information
Framework
*Shared Information and Data
Model SID*

Applications
Framework
*Telecom Applications Map
TAM*

Systems
Integration
Framework
*Technology Neutral
Architecture TNA*

Figure 1.5 – Four Core NGOSS Frameworks

At the highest level, NGOSS comprises four key frameworks and a supporting methodology for using those frameworks.

Business Process Framework - commonly known as the eTOM or the Enhanced Telecom Operations Map®

The eTOM defines all of the major business processes within and external to the enterprise. It provides the framework and common language of business processes that are used in the telecoms enterprise. It can be used to catalog existing processes within a service provider, act as a framework for defining scope of a software-based solution, or simply enable clearer lines of communication between a service provider and their system integrator. Details on how to understand the eTOM and how to make use of it within your environment are shown throughout this book.

Enterprise-wide Information Framework – commonly known as the SID or the Shared Information and Data Model

The SID provides a comprehensive common information model for the complete telecoms activities of an enterprise. It provides a "common language" for software developers and integrators to use in describing management information, which in turn allows easier and more effective integration across OSS/BSS software applications provided by multiple vendors. It provides the concepts and principles needed to define a shared information model, the elements or entities of the model, the business oriented UML class models, as well as design oriented UML class models and sequence diagrams to provide a system view of the information and data. While information models are challenging and complex conceptual models, this book attempts to dispel the complexity surrounding the SID and explains in simple terms how to grasp the SID and make use of it to help you meet your business needs.

Systems Integration Framework - commonly known as the TNA or the Technology-Neutral Architecture

The TNA defines the basic principles for developing an NGOSS based solution. This framework covers architectural issues including, common interfaces between components (called contract interfaces), distribution frameworks, common communications mechanisms and policy & process management. This architecture is intentionally called "Technology-Neutral" as it does not define how to implement the architecture, rather what principles must be applied for any particular technology specific implementation of NGOSS. Throughout this book, examples are given highlighting how to apply the NGOSS TNA in order to develop NGOSS based solutions.

Applications Framework - commonly known as the TAM or Telecom Application Map

The TAM has been developed as a working guide to help operators and their suppliers use a common reference Map and language to navigate the complex systems landscape that is typically found in fixed, mobile and cable operators. Where the Enhanced Telecom Operations Map® (eTOM) provides a framework of telecom processes, the Telecom Application Map provides a framework of telecom applications. The TAM is in the early stages of development within the TM Forum and is only mentioned here for completeness. However if the reader wishes to understand more about the TAM then they can download the early versions of it at www.tmforum.org. The TAM will not be covered in later chapters of this book.

NGOSS Methodology - commonly known as the SANRR Method

In addition to the core framework elements, NGOSS defines an iterative life cycle development methodology, commonly called SANRR (which refers to the five steps in the development methodology: **S**cope, **A**nalyze, **N**ormalize, **R**ationalize, **R**ectify). SANRR defines an approach for the analysis, specification, design, and implementation of solutions expressed in terms of NGOSS artifacts, such as the eTOM, SID, use cases, and contracts. SANRR is described in detail in later chapters of this book.

Chapter Two

NGOSS Distilled

This chapter provides an easy-to-understand summary of the TeleManagement Forum's New Generation Operations Systems and Software program (NGOSS).

NGOSS Explained

NGOSS captures the best practices and approaches of the telecoms and enterprise industries over the past decade, while discarding the worst. It has been developed by the telecommunications industry to meet the needs a variety of stakeholders, including service providers, equipment vendors, independent software vendors, and system integrators. By employing the cornerstones of a lean operator and its views, NGOSS embraces intelligent problem solving and holistic solution design. NGOSS maintains a solution's flexibility, enabling an enterprise to transform the way it operates. In short, NGOSS enables the transformation of the telecommunications industry.

An NGOSS solution can be characterized in a number of ways. NGOSS solutions are:

• Built on an approach that employs an iterative lifecycle development methodology

• Based on a common, federated information model

• Policy-enabled

• Process-driven

• Service-oriented.

The iterative lifecycle development methodology provides a way of defining a solution starting with a business challenge and carrying it through to an operating application. It is a systematic and formalized approach to specification and development with the final solution constructed using an iterative process. The lifecycle balances the concerns of all stakeholders via their involvement throughout the process.

Reusability leverages existing industry and corporate knowledge and functionality and promotes the identification and use of applications in multiple contexts. Building from a global knowledge base of experience enables an enterprise to create focused local solutions, reduces integration cost and time to market, as well as business and project related risks.

A common information model, called the Shared Information and Data (SID) model, provides a unifying information framework. This framework provides a definition of all assets and concerns and their relationships using the Unified Modeling Language (UML) as a formal modeling language. The framework provides a way to capture the information needs of all stakeholders by defining a common language for use across the business. It ensures traceability between business requirements and deployed solutions and can be used as the foundation for an application integration framework.

The SID links distributed and diverse information into a common structure and represents a holistic governance framework for controlling distributed problem solving. The SID supports interoperability across organizational, corporate, and regulatory boundaries. The SID has been structured to allow for federation of information. As a federated model, the SID draws on knowledge from other industry associations, standard bodies, authorities, and TM Forum member companies; it is not "home-grown". The organization of the SID framework enables a "divide and conquer" approach to problem solving. For example, information that characterizes network resources is organized into a single domain (Resource) within the SID.

NGOSS is policy-enabled, which means that policies are the mechanism for linking system control to business objectives. NGOSS provides visibility and access to business rules throughout applications developed using the NGOSS framework. A policy-enabled application provides the ability to modify process and system behavior based on a changing business environment reducing the time to make changes to an application. It allows policy makers at all levels to govern the behavior of applications and allows tuning of applications to improve organizational effectiveness.

As a process-driven framework, NGOSS provides an industry-wide business process framework, the Enhanced Telecom Operations Map® (eTOM), developed using a common modeling approach. The core of the eTOM framework provides a structured decomposition of process elements, exposing increasingly finer process element details at the lower levels of decomposition. The eTOM framework captures all of the process activity, as individual process elements, undertaken by a telecommunications service provider enterprise in one cohesive model. As such, the eTOM provides a common process language, a mechanism for process control and coordination, and facilitates chaining of process elements for end-to-end visibility of process flows. It improves the ability to re-use existing process implementations by other applications. The eTOM facilitates the extension of business processes across organizational and company boundaries.

NGOSS' service orientation decouples solution specifications from implementation technologies. Solution capabilities are delivered as a set of structured components via a mechanism that fully describes the interactions between the components. Service oriented architectures also provide a mechanism to identify and locate offered capabilities, implemented via contractual obligations between users of and providers of the service.

Employing the NGOSS development life cycle provides a number of very valuable and strategic benefits, including:

- Ensures the needs of all stakeholders are managed and controlled

- Provides traceability throughout the solution development lifecycle

- Enables change to be easily incorporated and the impact of change assessed

- Promotes progressive and collective understanding of the solution

- Defines clear roles for all stakeholders meaning a win for each

- Reduces the cost associated with application integration, sometimes referred to as the interoperability tax.

Figure 2.1 shows the component parts of NGOSS and depicts how they relate to the overall NGOSS life cycle. In the figure, the information architecture is represented by the Shared Information and Data model (SID), the process architecture is represented by the eTOM Business Process Framework, and the interaction architecture is represented by the Technology Neutral Architecture (TNA) which comprises contracts (a basic unit of interoperability) and components (which implement contracts).

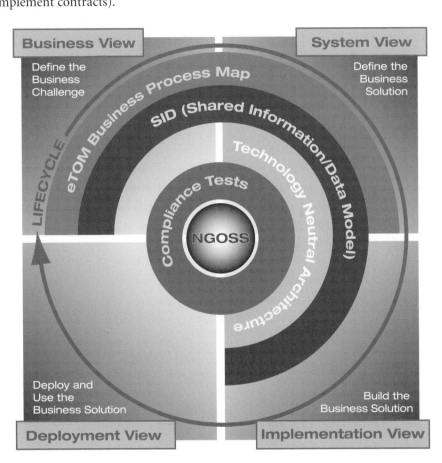

Figure 2.1 – NGOSS Life Cycle

NGOSS builds on industry best practices and foundations, organizes relevant information so that it is useful to all stakeholders and maintains integrity of solutions throughout their lifecycle, while allowing "what-if" analysis across the lifecycle. NGOSS works to put policy and process control in the hands of the business while providing a collaborative and balanced approach to development for all stakeholders.

NOTE: This book focuses on the TM Forum's development of the NGOSS business and system views. Other industry groups, such as the OSS through Java™ Initiative, focus on the implementation and deployment views.

NGOSS Lifecycle & SANRR Methodology Explained

The NGOSS Lifecycle and SANRR Methodology provides a common framework that describes how to use and deploy NGOSS within an organization. The NGOSS Lifecycle employs all NGOSS artifacts. It uses the eTOM business process framework, the SID, and the Technology-Neutral Architecture (TNA) to provide an approach to development that covers process definition, system design, solution implementation, and solution deployment. Development progresses through the four NGOSS views in a sequential yet iterative manner.

NGOSS Lifecycle Overview

A number of fundamental principles govern the overall NGOSS Lifecycle, including:

• There are different communities, such as service providers, independent software vendors, system integrators, equipment vendors, users, business analysts, developers, and so forth, interested in NGOSS; each community must be able to look at an NGOSS solution from their own viewpoint

• NGOSS artifacts are transformed or morphed as they move from one view to another; associations exist between the artifacts in each view

• Use cases are evident in each NGOSS view

• Contracts, which are comprised of one or more use cases, are the basic unit of interoperability; a contract is a container that collects and carries information throughout the lifecycle

• Traceability and visibility provide a means to verify that required business, system, and implementation processes, policies and functionalities are realized (forward traceability)

• Traceability and visibility throughout the lifecycle are necessary to ensure that running and available services meet the specified needs of the business (backward traceability)

• An information model (the SID) is shared throughout the lifecycle as a common underlying foundation for all models; it is essential to assure specified requirements, processes, policies, and constraints can interoperate and are traceable.

The NGOSS Lifecycle embodies a number of characteristics present in other frameworks and methodologies, including:

• Zachman Framework – emphasis on the enterprise and a business model influenced the definition of a NGOSS business view within the lifecycle

• Model-Driven Architecture – separation of business and technology concerns influenced the generation of downstream artifacts from an architectural model, such as the SID

• Reference Model for Open Distributed Programming – separation of viewpoints influenced the definition of the NGOSS business, system, implementation, and deployment views

• Unified Software Development Process – use case driven, iterative approach influenced the presence of use cases in all four NGOSS views.

NGOSS Lifecycle & SANRR Methodology Explained

The NGOSS SANRR methodology defines an approach for the analysis, specification, design, and implementation of solutions expressed in terms of NGOSS artifacts, such as the eTOM, SID, use cases, and contracts. SANRR embodies aspects of Zachman, Model-Driven Architecture, the Reference Model for Open Distributed Programming, as well as the Unified Software Development Process.

Five iterative steps comprise the NGOSS SANRR methodology:

• Scope

• Analyze

• Normalize

• Rationalize

• Rectify.

The Scope step defines the solution boundary by understanding and documenting the business purpose of the solution, the current business environment, and the future business environment. Scope assures that the goals, missions, and objectives of the solution are consistent throughout the lifecycle, beginning with the business view and continuing on to the deployment view.

The Analyze step prepares detailed documentation of the current business environment and the future environment for a solution. Documentation includes processes, information, and policies within the current and future environment. This step also serves as preparation for the subsequent identification of missing or duplicated functionality.

Normalize facilitates the interoperation of different physical views based on the same logical view by ensuring all components map to a common language (the SID) and defining extensions to the SID as needed.

Rationalize identifies new processes, policies, functionalities, and technologies that need to be designed, developed, and/or deployed to support the new business environment. Any duplicate functionality is identified. If any changes or additions to the new business environment are identified, the next step, Rectify, may commence to fill identified gaps, or the process may return to the Scope step if a redefinition of the new business environment is needed. Mapping the current business environment, such as current processes, to the future environment identifies gaps to be filled.

The Rectify step provides new processes, policies, and functionality to fill gaps identified during the Rationalize step that modify existing functionality, processes, and policies to meet the needs of the new business environment and/or to eliminate redundant functionality. The Figure 2.2 shows the relationship among the SANRR methodology steps.

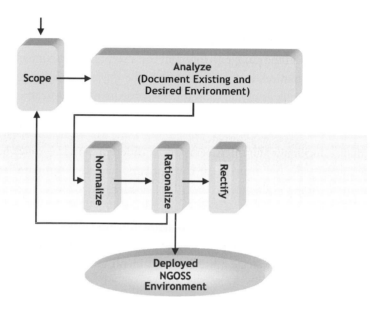

Figure 2.2 – NGOSS SANRR Methodology Flow

NGOSS Perspectives and Views

A distinguishing factor of the NGOSS Lifecycle is the concept of perspectives and views. Two categories of recognized perspectives are:

• Logical and physical

• Service provider and service developer.

As mentioned earlier, the four views fundamental to a lean operator are:

• Business view

• System view

• Implementation view

• Deployment view.

Each perspective is comprised of a subset of the four views as shown in Figure 2.3 and is described in the paragraphs that follow the figure.

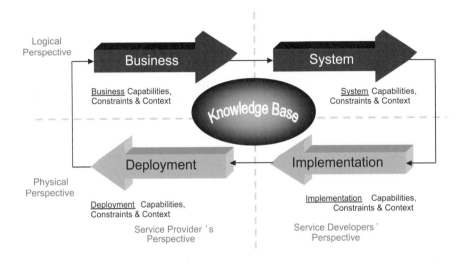

Figure 2.3 – Views Developed by the NGOSS Lifecycle

The logical and physical perspectives enable the separation of the logical (technology-neutral business and system views) and the physical (technology-specific implementation and deployment views). This separates the definition of a solution (logical perspective) from the implementation and deployed instances of the solution (physical perspective). This facilitates the development and deployment of multiple solutions from a single solution definition.

The service provider's and service developer's perspectives cross the views of interest in the other perspectives. A service provider's interest in the logical perspective's business view relates to the statement of the solution in terms the provider can understand. The provider's interest in the physical perspective's deployment view relates to the operating application that is used to implement the provider's business processes. A service developer's interest in the logical perspective's system view is defined in terms the developer uses to craft a solution;

the developer's interest in the physical perspective's implementation view pertains to the technologies the developer uses to realize a solution.

The four views provide traceability from a statement of business requirements, through a business definition of a solution through to its system, implementation and deployment via the evolution/transformation of artifacts in the knowledge base (shown in the figure), such as the eTOM, the SID, and the Technology-Neutral Architecture.

The NGOSS Lifecycle defines the four views that characterize a lean operator as

• NGOSS Business View – the focus is on business processes, information, and their interaction. The eTOM and SID, used together, identify and express the business processes as well as the business entities that interact in order to support one or more business goals

• NGOSS System View – the focus is on objects, behaviors, and computational interactions; the system view, also expressed in terms of the eTOM and SID, defines system capabilities in the form of system contracts which describe the exchange of information among collaborating entities that make up a solution

• NGOSS Implementation View – the focus is on how to build software, hardware, and firmware that will implement the solution being designed; it maps a technology-neutral specification of the solution to a targeted architecture

• NGOSS Deployment View – the focus is on operating and actively monitoring the solution to ensure that its behavior meets expectations.

Use Cases and Contracts – Two Key NGOSS Interaction Artifacts

Two key NGOSS artifacts, the eTOM and SID, at times overshadow two other key artifacts, use cases and contracts, which are also present in each NGOSS view. They represent the interaction between the information contained in the SID and the processes contained within the eTOM. Details of the Interaction Architecture are explained in a later section of this chapter. However, it is important to explain their place within the NGOSS Lifecycle.

Use cases describe, through a series of interactions, an agreement between the stakeholders (actors) of a system and the system itself. The agreement described in the use case defines the expected behavior of the system along with any material, services, and other items or functionality that are exchanged between the stakeholders and the system. It also describes, through reference to other use cases, different scenarios that can arise and the behavior represented by the different scenarios.

Since the four different NGOSS views each focus on different aspects of the overall solution, use cases are present in each of the views. Each use case is defined using a set of core elements along with a new set of elements added to reflect its focus within each view. The invariant (core) elements of a use case enable them to be related to each other, while the changeable elements reflect new phases and/or options used in building and/or delivering the overall solution.

A business use case defines the steps to achieve a business goal, services to be provided by the solution, and the high level methods of operation. As the system view develops, a use case may be further decomposed to simplify/focus on goals to be achieved. Mapping a system view use case to specific target technologies brings rise to one or more implementation view use cases. Deployment view use cases guide the installer, operations personnel, administrative personnel, and other actors in the installation, deployment, monitoring, and overall management of the solution.

NGOSS contracts represent the fundamental unit of interoperability in an NGOSS solution. A contract is derived from one (typically) or more use cases. Interoperability is achieved for each of the four views defined in the NGOSS Lifecycle through the consistent use of the contract. A contract is a specification of a service to be delivered, as well as a specification for the information and code that implements the service.

What this means is that a contract has its own lifecycle, enabling the specification and implementation of its functionality to evolve through each NGOSS view as shown in Figure 2.4.

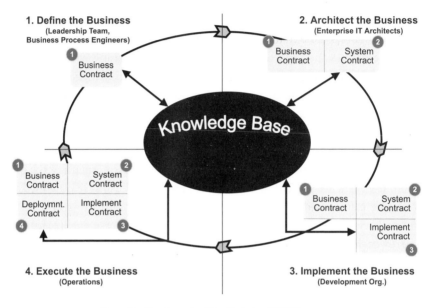

Figure 2.4 – Transformation (Morphing) of an NGOSS Contract

The business view of a contract specifies the high-level goals and obligations that a resource and/or service must supply. This is done using concepts (business entities, processes, and use cases) understandable to the business community.

The system view of a contract specifies the architectural requirements necessary to implement the contract, as defined in the business view. This is done in a technical, though technology-neutral, manner.

The implementation view of a contract specifies the configuration, programming, and other implementation factors of the components necessary to provide the functionality specific in the contract. This is done in one or more technology-specific ways, using vendor-specific devices and languages as necessary.

The deployment view of a contract specifies mechanisms for monitoring the performance, cost, and other aspects of the functionality delivered by the contract. It ensures that if the contractual obligations of the contract are violated, appropriate corrective action can and is taken.

The Need for a Business Process Framework

Traditionally in the telecommunications industry, service providers delivered end-to-end services to their customers. As such, the entire value chain was controlled by a single enterprise, if necessary via interconnection arrangements with other service providers, where customers desired access out of the geographic regions controlled by the service provider. However in a liberalized marketplace, service providers have to respond both to the customer's increased demands for superior customer service and to stiffer competition. They have therefore been driven to expand their markets beyond their self-contained boundaries and to broaden their business relationships.

Service providers now face very different regulatory environments and their business strategies and approaches to competition are quite distinct, nevertheless they share several common characteristics:

• Heavily dependent upon effective management of information and communications networks to stay competitive

• Adopting a service management approach to the way they run their business and their networks

• Moving to more of an end-to-end Process Management approach developed from the customer's point of view

• Automating their Customer Care, Service and Network Management Processes

• Needing to integrate new BSS/OSS with legacy systems

• Focusing on data services offerings

• Focusing on total service performance, including customer satisfaction

• Integrating current technology (for example, SDH/SONET and ATM) and new technologies (for example, IP and DWDM)

• Emphasizing more of a "buy" rather than "build" approach that integrates systems from multiple suppliers.

Some service providers choose to operate their own network and/or information technology infrastructure, while others choose to outsource this segment of their business. The effective exploitation of this information technology and network infrastructure, whether directly operated or outsourced, is an integral part of the service delivery chain and directly influences the service quality and cost perceived by the end customer. Service providers need to become skilled at assessing outsourcing opportunities whether in information technology and/or network infrastructure areas or other areas and then, be skilled at integrating and managing any outsourcing arrangements.

To meet both existing and new demands, service providers still urgently require well-automated operations processes whether they are incumbent providers or new entrants. Some service providers struggle with high growth from a start-up phase, others with the commoditization of key cash-cow services, and yet others with the move from a manually-intensive, inconsistent, inflexible environment to one that provides significant improvement in customer focus, service quality, unit cost, and time to market. Service providers have to pervasively do business electronically with trading partners, suppliers and wholesale and retail customers. For the growing mobile/wireless and IP services markets, these service providers are focused on quickly provisioning new customers and supporting service quality issues, while continually reducing development and operating costs. For all service providers, there is an intense drive to introduce both new value-added services and dramatic improvements in customer support. There is also an increasing need for service providers to manage the integration required in mergers and acquisitions activity due to the consolidation trend the industry is now experiencing.

For the full range of service providers and network operators, the leading focus of the TM Forum's mission is to enable end-to-end process automation of the businesses operational processes that deliver information and communications services. The eTOM business process framework is one of the NGOSS frameworks used to accomplish this mission.

The purpose of the eTOM framework is to continue to set a vision for the industry to compete successfully through the implementation of business process driven approaches to managing the enterprise. This includes ensuring integration among all vital enterprise support systems concerned with service delivery and support. The focus of the eTOM framework is on the business processes used by service providers, the linkages between these processes, the identification of interfaces, and the use of Customer, Service, Resource, Supplier/Partner and other information by multiple processes. Exploitation of information from every corner of the business will be essential to success in the future. In an ebusiness environment, automation to gain productivity enhancement, increased revenue and better customer relationships is vital. Perhaps at no other time has process automation been so critical to success in the marketplace. The over-arching objective of the eTOM framework is to continue to build on TM Forum's success in establishing:

• An 'industry standard' business process framework

• Common definitions to describe process elements of a service provider

• Agreement on the basic information required to perform each process element within a business activity, and use of this within the overall NGOSS program for business requirements and information model development that can guide industry agreement on contract interfaces, shared information and data model elements, and supporting system infrastructure and products

- The eTOM Business Process Framework and the associated business process modeling, describes for an enterprise the process elements and their relationship that are involved in information and communications services and technologies management. Additionally, the points of interconnection that make up the end-to-end, operational process flows for Fulfillment, Assurance, Billing within the Operations process area, and for Strategy, Infrastructure & Product process area are addressed by the eTOM.

Service providers need this common framework of processes to enable them to do business efficiently and effectively with other entities and to enable the development and use of third-party software without the need for major customization. In an ebusiness environment, this common understanding of process is critical to managing the more complex business relationships of today's information and communications services marketplace. ebusiness integration among enterprises seems to be most successful through strong process integration. Recent industry fallout, particularly in relation to dotcoms, does not reduce the pressure for ebusiness automation – it strengthens the need to capitalize on ebusiness opportunities to be successful.

However, the eTOM business process framework is not just an ecommerce or ebusiness process framework; it supports traditional business processes with the integration of ebusiness.

What is the eTOM?

The eTOM is a business process framework, that is, a reference framework or model for categorizing all the business activities that a service provider will use. It is not a service provider business model. In other words, it does not address the strategic issues or questions of who a service provider's target customers should be, what market segments should the service provider serve, what are a service provider's vision, mission, and so forth. A business process framework is one part of the strategic business model and plan for a service provider.

The eTOM business process framework is better regarded as a business process framework, rather than a business process model, since its aim is to categorize the process elements and business activities so that these can then be combined in many different ways, to implement end-to-end business processes (for example, fulfillment, assurance, billing) which deliver value for the customer and the service provider.

Service providers, as well as system integrators, application service providers and vendors are already working with the eTOM business process framework. They need an industry standard framework for procuring software and equipment, as well as to interface with other service providers in an increasingly complex network of business relationships. Many service providers have contributed their own process models because they recognize the need to have a broader industry framework that doesn't just address operations or traditional business processes.

The TM Forum initially identified business processes as a consensus tool for discussion and agreement among service providers and network operators. This encouraged convergence and general support for a broad common base in this area, which has been built on and extended with the eTOM framework, to enable:

• Focused work to be carried out in TM Forum teams to define detailed business requirements, information agreements, business application contracts and shared information and data model specifications (exchanges between applications or systems) and to review these outputs for consistency

• Relating business needs to available or required standards

• A common process view for equipment suppliers, applications builders and integrators to build management systems by combining third party and in-house developments.

The anticipated result is that the products purchased by service providers and network operators for business and operational management of their networks, information technologies and services will integrate better into their environment, enabling the cost benefits of end-to-end automation. Furthermore, a common industry view on processes and information facilitates operator-to-operator, operator-to-customer, and operator-to-supplier/partner process interconnection, which is essential for rapid service provisioning and problem handling in a competitive global environment. This process interconnection is the key to ebusiness supply chain management in particular.

The eTOM work also provides the definition of common terms concerning enterprise processes, sub-processes and the activities performed within each. Common terminology makes it easier for service providers to negotiate with customers, third party suppliers, and other service providers.

The eTOM Framework

Figure 2.5 shows the highest conceptual view of the eTOM framework. This view provides an overall context of the key concepts within the framework.

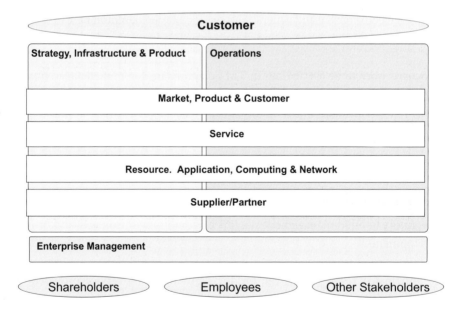

Figure 2.5 - eTOM Business Process Framework – Level 0 Key Concepts

The framework differentiates strategy and lifecycle processes from the operations processes in two large process areas, seen as the two major boxes in the upper part of the diagram. It also differentiates the key functional areas as horizontal layers across these process areas. The third major process area, concerned with management of the enterprise itself, is shown as a separate box in the lower part of the diagram. In addition, Figure 2.5 also shows the internal and external entities that interact with the enterprise (as ovals).

Figure 2.6 shows how the three major process areas – designated as Level 0 processes of the eTOM business process framework - are decomposed into their constituent Level 1 process groupings. This view thus provides the Level 1 decomposition of the Level 0 processes and gives an overall view of the eTOM framework.

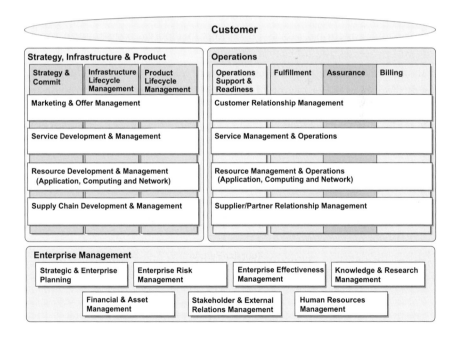

Figure 2.6 - eTOM Business Process Framework - Level 1 Processes

Figure 2.6 also shows seven end-to-end vertical process groupings, which are the end-to-end processes that are required to support customers and to manage the business. Among these end-to-end Vertical Process Groupings, the focal point of the eTOM framework is on the core customer operations processes of Fulfillment, Assurance and Billing (FAB). Operations Support & Readiness (OSR) is differentiated from FAB real-time processes to highlight the focus on enabling support and automation in FAB, that is, on-line and immediate support of customers, with OSR ensuring that the operational environment is in place to let the FAB processes do their job. Outside of the Operations process area - in the Strategy, Infrastructure & Product (SIP) process area - the Strategy & Commit vertical, as well as the two Lifecycle Management verticals, are differentiated. These are distinct because, unlike Operations, they do not directly support the customer, are intrinsically different from the Operations processes and work on different business time cycles.

The horizontal functional process groupings in Figure 2.6 distinguish functional operations processes and other types of business functional processes, for example, Marketing versus Selling, Service Development versus Service Configuration, and so forth. Among these Horizontal Functional Process Groupings, those on the left (that cross the Strategy & Commit, Infrastructure Lifecycle Management and Product Lifecycle Management vertical process groupings) support the work in the Operations process area.

As can be seen in Figure 2.6, the eTOM framework provides the following benefits:

• It provides a scope addressing all enterprise processes

• It distinctly identifies marketing processes to reflect their heightened importance in an ebusiness world

• It distinctly identifies Enterprise Management processes, and places them in context with the other operations processes

• It brings Fulfillment, Assurance and Billing (FAB) onto the high-level framework view to emphasize the customer priority processes as the focus of the enterprise

• It recognizes three vertical process groupings within the enterprise that are distinctly different from the vertical process groupings in the Operations process area by separately identifying the SIP process area. The three vertical process groupings are Strategy & Commit, Infrastructure Lifecycle Management and Product Lifecycle Management.

• It recognizes the different cycle times of the strategy and lifecycle management processes and the need to separate these processes from the customer priority operations processes where automation is most critical. Decoupling the Strategy & Commit and the two Lifecycle Management processes from the customer operations processes accomplishes this.

• It moves from the older customer care or service orientation to a customer relationship management orientation that allows for customer self-management and control, increasing the value customers contribute to the enterprise and the use of information to customize and personalize to the individual customer. It adds more elements to this customer operations functional layer to represent better the selling processes and to integrate marketing fulfillment within Customer Relationship Management. Note that Customer Relationship Management within the eTOM framework is very broadly defined and larger in scope than some definitions of CRM.

• It acknowledges the need to manage resources across technologies, (application, computing and network resources), by integrating the Network and Systems Management functional process into Resource Management & Operations. It also moves the management of IT into this functional layer as opposed to having a separate process grouping.

• It recognizes that the enterprise interacts with external parties, and that the enterprise may need to interact with process flows defined by external parties, as in ebusiness interactions.

Figure 2.7 shows the eTOM level 2 processes in the Operations process area. Other process areas of the eTOM are similarly decomposed.

The eTOM has evolved since the inception of the TM Forum's NGOSS program to include a number of other artifacts, in addition to levels of decomposition down to level three.

These newer artifacts represent the interaction among eTOM processes and SID business entities defined using a number of techniques that develop:

• Process flow diagrams

• Activity diagrams

• Use case diagrams

• State chart diagrams

• Sequence diagrams.

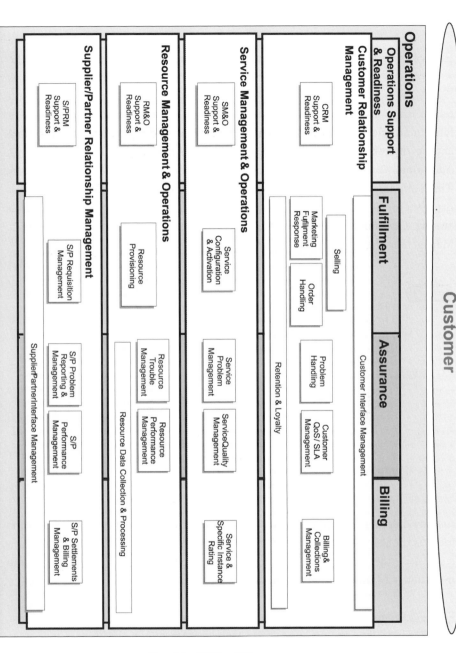

Figure 2.7 – eTOM Level 2 Processes

Each of these techniques and its purpose is explained below.

Figure 2.8 shows an example of a process flow diagram. These diagrams depict the relationships among processes from an execution perspective. Understanding the flows among the process elements facilitates the understanding of interactions among organizations that are responsible for the individual process elements. Additionally, understanding the flows is important when building applications, which support the processes, as the flows represent interaction between various components of an application or applications. This figure depicts the interactions among Customer Relationship Management processes and links to Service Management and Operations processes.

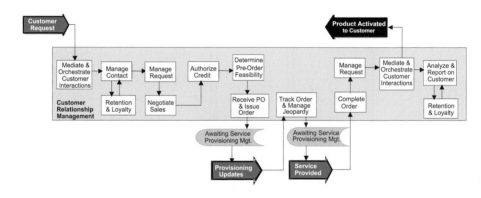

Figure 2.8 – eTOM Process Flow Diagram

Activity diagrams are useful in showing the interactions among processes where the focus is on a single object, such as a service order, or a group of objects, such as a customer order and a service order. These interactions form the basis for the interchange of information among NGOSS contracts.

Figure 2.9 depicts more detailed interactions among processes within Customer Relationship Management and Service Management and Operations.

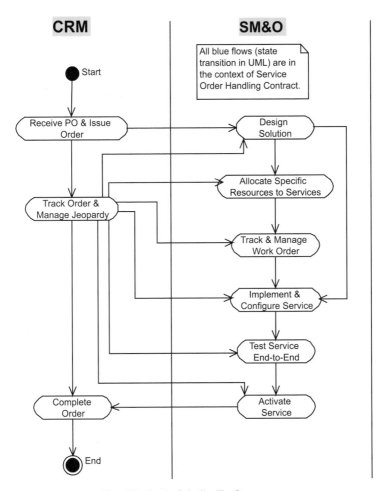

Figure 2.9 – Service Order Handling Processes

Use cases begin to describe the interaction between a user (actor) and an application (system). As such, use cases begin to define the functional characteristics of a system. The definition of each use case further defines the interaction between a user and an application.

Figure 2.10 depicts some of the use cases involved with managing the lifecycle of a service order.

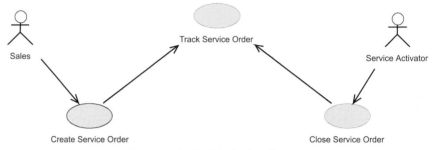

Figure 2.10 - Service Order Use Case Diagram

Process decomposition, process flow analysis, activity analysis, and use case modeling all contribute to the definition of the states through which an object, such as a service order, moves. The state chart diagram in Figure 2.11 depicts the states through which a service order moves and the movement from state to state. As such, it defines business rules under which a service order handling process (and its resultant implementation) must operate. State chart diagrams are also useful in identifying any missing processes and/or use cases. There must be a process and/or use case that moves an object, such as a service order, from one state to the next. Additionally, state chart diagrams are useful in identifying and confirming entities, attributes, and associations within an information model that represents a service order.

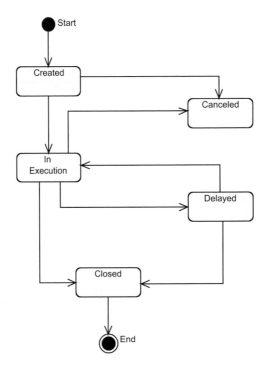

Figure 2.11 - Service Order Lifecycle States

Sequence diagrams depict the interaction among actors (users), use cases, classes, such as service order and customer order, and objects (instances of classes). These diagrams can be considered as part of the eTOM's system view. In Figure 2.12 the interaction is between actors (stick figures) and classes (boxes). The lines between the actors and classes represent messages exchanged between actors and classes and between the Customer Order and Service Order classes. The messages exchanged represent the inputs and outputs of NGOSS contracts. A more detailed discussion of contracts is contained in the Interaction Architecture section of this chapter.

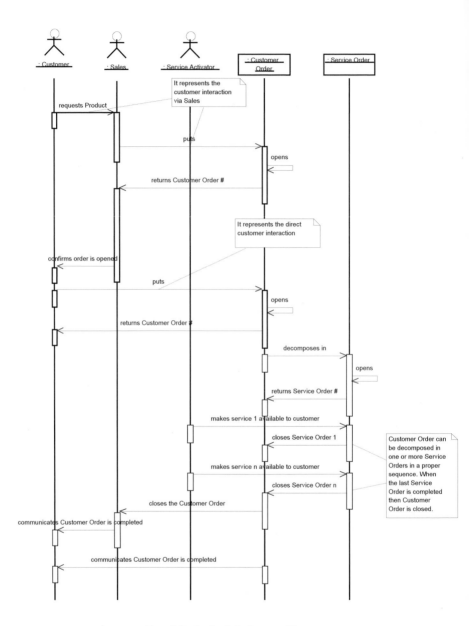

Figure 2.12 – Service Order Sequence Diagram

SID Explained

For many years the eTOM, and its predecessor the TOM, have provided a business process reference framework and common business process vocabulary. This framework and vocabulary have provided the communications and information industry enterprises an effective way to organize their business processes and communicate with each other.

The Shared Information and Data (SID) business view model can be viewed as a companion model to the eTOM, in that it provides an information and data reference model and a common information and data vocabulary from a business entity perspective. The business view model uses the concepts of domains and aggregate business entities (or sub-domains) to categorize business entities, so as to reduce duplication and overlap. This partitioning of the SID business view model also allows distributed work teams to build out the model definitions while minimizing the flow-on impacts across the model.

Teamed with the eTOM, the SID model provides enterprises with not only a process view of their business but also an entity view. That is to say, the SID provides the definition of the 'things' that are to be affected by the business processes defined in the eTOM. Within NGOSS, the SID and eTOM in combination offer a way to explain 'how' things are intended to fit together to meet a given business need.

SID Business View

The SID business view focuses on business entity definitions and associated attribute definitions. A business entity is a thing of interest to the business, while its attributes are facts that further describe the entity. Together the definitions provide a business-oriented perspective of the information and data. When combined with business oriented UML class models and XML schema, the definitions provide the business view of the information and data.

The content in the SID business view is organized using the SID Model Framework. The SID Framework was developed by the application of data affinity concepts to an enterprise's processes and data to derive a non-redundant view of the enterprise's shared information and data. The result of this analysis is a layered framework, which partitions the shared information and data.

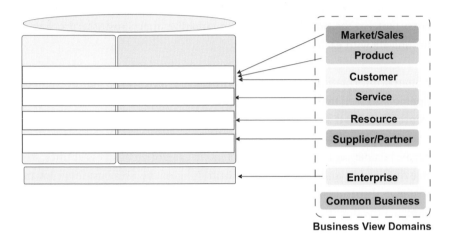

Figure 2.13 – SID Framework Domains Aligned With eTOM Domains

At the top layer, a set of domains is identified which are broadly aligned with the eTOM business process framework as shown in Figure 2.13.

A **Domain** is a collection of Aggregate Business Entities associated with a specific management area. Domains that make up the SID Framework are consistent with eTOM level 0 concepts.

Domains are derived from an analysis of Process and Information Frameworks and have the following properties:

• Contain business entities that encapsulate both operations and corporate/enterprise information

• Are relatively stable collections of corporate/enterprise data and associated operations (in comparison with processes)

• Provide for robustness of corporate/enterprise data formats

• Provide clear responsibility and ownership.

An **Aggregate Business Entity (ABE)** is a well-defined set of information and operations that characterize a highly cohesive, loosely coupled set of business entities.

A **Business Entity** represents something of interest to the business that may be tangible (such as a customer), active (such as a customer order), or conceptual (such as a customer account). Business entities are characterized by attributes and participate in relationships with other business entities. Business entity instances typically move through a well-defined life cycle.

An **attribute** is a fact that describes a business entity, such as a customer account number.

A **relationship** is an association of business interest between two business entities, such as a customer resides at an address, or between a business entity and itself.

Within each domain there is a high degree of cohesion between the identified business entities, and loose coupling between different domains. This enables segmentation of the total business problem and allows effort to be focused on a particular domain of interest. The use of the resultant business entity definitions within each domain, when used in conjunction with the eTOM business process framework, provides a business view of the shared information and data.

Within each domain, further partitioning of the information is achieved through the identification of Aggregate Business Entities (ABE's). Figure 2.14 shows the currently identified Level 1 ABE's. As the SID business view is further expanded and defined, further partitioning of the ABE's occurs as more explicit business entities are identified.

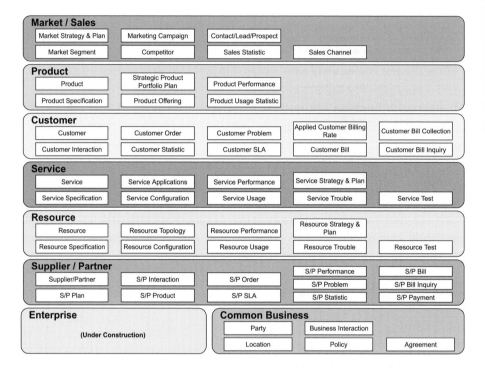

Figure 2.14 - SID Domains & Level 1 ABEs

The business entities along with the attributes and relationships that characterize the entities provide a view of the model that is easily understood from a business perspective. The business entities, attributes, and relationships are progressively developed using textual descriptions in each SID addendum and in a consolidated UML-based model. The UML model provides an architecturally oriented business view of business entities, their attributes, and relationships to other business entities.

Figure 2.15 shows an example of a SID domain definition and definitions of some of its ABEs. It also shows the relationship between the SID entities and the eTOM processes. The Primary eTOM Level 2 process refers to the eTOM level 2 process that manages the lifecycle of the relevant SID ABE. The Secondary eTOM level 2 processes are other processes that use the informationassociated with the relevant SID ABE.

The **Customer** Domain includes all data and operations associated with individuals or organizations that obtain products from an enterprise, such as a service provider. It represents all types of contact with the customer, the management of the relationship, and the administration of customer data. The Customer Domain also includes data and contract operations related to the customer bills for products, collection of payment, overdue accounts, and the billing inquiries and adjustments made as a result of inquiries.

Customer ABEs	Primary Vertical eTOM Process Groupings	Primary eTOM Level 2 Processes	Secondary eTOM Level 2 Processes
Customer Is the focus for the Customer domain. Customer data is the enterprise's knowledge of the customer and accounts held by a customer.	CRM – F	Selling	Product Marketing Communications & Promotion
			Order Handling
			Problem Handling
			Customer QoS/SLA Management
			Billing & Collections Management
			Retention & Loyalty
			Customer Interface Management
Customer Interaction Represents communications with customers, and the translation of customer requests and inquiries into appropriate "events" such as the creation of an customer order, the creation of a customer bill inquiry, or the creation of a customer problem.	CRM – FAB	Customer Interface Management	Selling
			Order Handling
			Problem Handling
			Customer QoS/SLA Management
			Billing & Collections Management
			Retention & Loyalty

Figure 2.15 - SID Domain and ABE Definitions

The sources for the SID model include a variety of industry models, as well as models contributed by TM Forum member organizations. Where time permitted the contents of the SID model were mapped to the source models. Complete synthesis of the content of all models to find a common term for a concept was not possible. A best attempt was made to list cross-references to source models and synonyms for terms as part of the definition of the SID business entities.

As the development of the SID model has progressed, subsequent levels of ABEs have been identified, just as in the development of the eTOM where subsequent levels of processes were identfied. As an example, Figure 2.16 shows level 2 ABEs identified within the Service domain.

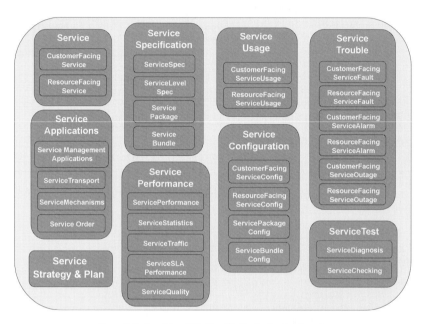

Figure 2.16 - Level Two ABEs identified in the Service Domain

At some point in the decomposition of ABEs, business entities appear within the ABEs. Business entities represent the lowest level of entity decomposition within the SID Framework. The SID Framework, along with business entities, the entities' attributes and associations are organized into a UML model as shown in Figure 2.17.

Figure 2.17 shows the ABEs, which comprise the SID Customer domain. Also illustrated are the entities that make up the Applied Customer Billing Rate ABE, along with the Applied Customer Billing Rate entity's attributes and associations.

SID Phase VI Models
  Use Case View
  Logical View
    Common Business Entities
    Customer Domain
      Applied Customer Billing Rate ABE
        AppliedCustomerBillingCharge
        AppliedCustomerBillingAllowance
        AppliedCustomerBillingCredit
        AppliedCustomerBillingDiscount
        AppliedCustomerBillingProductAlteration
        AppliedCustomerBillingProductCharge
        AppliedCustomerBillingProductUsageRate
        AppliedCustomerBillingRate
          date
          quantity
          description
          theCompositeAppliedCustomerBillingRate (CompositeAppliedCustomerBillingRate)
          theCustomerAccount (CustomerAccount)
          theAppliedCustomerBillingTaxRate (AppliedCustomerBillingTaxRate)
          theAppliedCustomerBillingProductAlteration (AppliedCustomerBillingProductAlteration)
          theCustomerBill (CustomerBill)
        AppliedCustomerBillingRebate
        AppliedCustomerBillingTaxRate
        AtomicAppliedCustomerBillingRate
        CompositeAppliedCustomerBillingRate
        Associations
      Customer ABE
      Customer Addendum Figures
      Customer Bill ABE
      Customer Interaction ABE
      Customer Order ABE
      Customer Service Level Agreement ABE
      Customer Statistic ABE
      Version - Customer Domain
      Associations

Figure 2.17 – SID Framework and Entities Within a UML Model

Business entities, their associations and attributes are depicted graphically using UML class diagrams as shown in Figure 2.18.

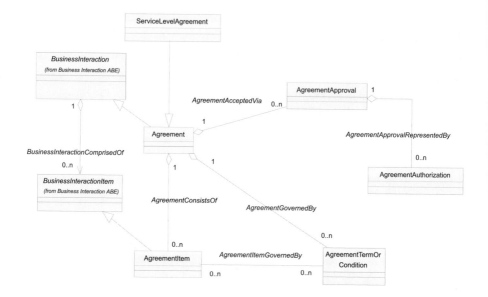

Figure 2.18 - SID Businesa Enties and thier Assosiations

The rectangles in Figure 2.18 represent SID business entities and the lines between the entities represent associations between the entities. The numbers and letters on each association represent the cardinality of the associations. For example, an Agreement consists of zero to an unlimited (n) number of AgreementItems; each AgreementItem is contained on one (1) Agreement.

SID System View

Thus far, the SID model represented here represents the NGOSS business view. The SID system view extends the SID business view by adding additional details about a business entity. These details include additional attributes, operations, and association classes as shown in Figure 2.19.

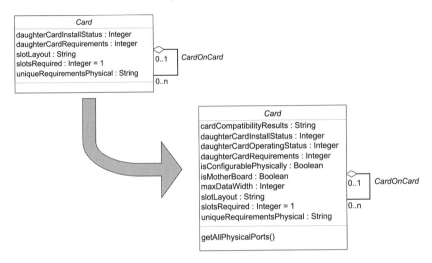

Figure 2.19 – SID System View Entity, Attributes and Operations

In Figure 2.19, additional attributes, such as cardCompatibilityResults, were added in the system view; an operation getAllPhysicalPorts was also added.

There is also an implementation view of the SID. This view transforms the SID system view into a data model. Currently there is no implementation view of the SID within NGOSS. However, other industry groups, such as the OSS through Java™ Initiative, are developing implementation views of the SID.

Technology-Neutral Architecture (Interaction Architecture) Explained

One of the major guidelines in the definition of the NGOSS Architecture is to ensure that it remains valid independent of the specific implementation technology which will be used to implement the NGOSS solution. For this reason the NGOSS Architecture is known as the "Technology-Neutral Architecture – TNA".

The Technology-Neutral Architecture sets out a set of principles and approaches for defining a component-based, distributed systems architecture and an associated critical set of system services that this architecture requires. At a high level these aspects include:

- Separation of business process from component implementation

- Presence of a security-enabled architecture

- Presence of a policy-enabled architecture

- A shared information and data environment (already presented as the SID)

- Distribution transparency.

Describing these in more detail:

Separation of Business Process from Component Implementation

The fundamental unit of interoperability in an NGOSS system is the contract which is a technology neutral representation of an interface to a service. The basic premise of the NGOSS architecture is the identification of well-defined, contract-specified interfaces, implemented by commercial off-the-shelf components and supported by a distributed processing framework. This makes it possible to build a highly scalable, extremely flexible OSS that enables and facilitates the rapid deployment of new service products.

A process management service coordinates access to NGOSS components. This service provides externalized process control to make decisions or execute decisions that control which business contracts (implemented as components) need to be invoked and the order of their invocation. Each decision is based on a number of factors, including the process plan, which includes policies, product definitions, and service level agreements, the outcome of the previous contract invocations, the states of the pertinent business and functional service components, and the availability of business contract instances of the next business contract type required for invocation.

Security-Enabled Architecture

Security is essential to the development of NGOSS systems and should not be considered as an add-on to be incorporated at a later date. Security capabilities must be pervasive throughout the NGOSS environment and must be woven into NGOSS system solutions from the outset.

A security-enabled architecture ensures that confidential information generated by or relating to a user is adequately protected against misuse or misappropriation. Organizations and their employees should be adequately protected from internal and external threats when operating an NGOSS environment. There are clear lines of responsibility between entities, both inter- and intra-enterprise, so that liability for resources and services can be attributed and accounted for. Resources and services provided by networks and environments should be adequately protected against misuse or misappropriation. The level of protection afforded to users and providers of services should follow best practices available to the telecommunications industry. Implementation of NGOSS security features and mechanisms can be extended and enhanced as required by new threats and services.

Policy-Enabled Architecture

Users, applications, services, and resources of an NGOSS system may be categorized by their role(s), which define the set of resources and services to which they have access. Policies may be used to determine which role(s) an entity, user, or resource is assigned, as well as to dynamically determine the specific set of resources and services to which a given role has access. Policies may be used to alter the set of resources and services, or otherwise constrain them, based on dynamic conditions in the managed environment. The net effect is that an entity may be denied access to, or use of, all or part of another entity to which it should normally have access. The NGOSS policy subsystem supervises operations being carried out by all other services that it manages. Hence, the Policy Management Framework services can apply constraints and/or conditions on what operations to execute, as well as when, by whom, and how they are executed within an NGOSS system. These constraints can be used to impose local rules on processing sequences and conditions that are required to be met before (pre-conditions) and after (post-conditions and exceptions) any action.

Policy and process management each have their advantages. Policy management prescribes declarative control of the system, while process management is more imperative in nature. The notion "behavior and control" is defined to represent the balance between policy and process management. Behavior connotes a way of describing how an entity responds to a certain set of conditions, while control is defined as the use of a set of mechanisms to direct how a particular behavior is managed or executed. Policy and process management should both be present in an NGOSS system.

Each discrete system capability can be constrained by any applicable policy rules. From an architectural perspective, the NGOSS policy subsystem is an integral segment of the overall NGOSS system architecture. This enables a policy to be mapped onto one or more technologies, meaning a policy can be constructed using the most advantageous technology available. This future-proofs policy definitions by separating their specification from their implementation.

Distribution Transparency

NGOSS clients as well as components need to locate other NGOSS contracts and the components that implement them without knowledge of their physical location in the network. This is called distribution transparency.

The essential framework entity that supports distribution transparency is the repository. The repository enables a naming service, a registrations service, and a contract location service. These services interoperate to provide distributed storage, management, and retrieval of NGOSS information, such as contracts, shared information and data objects, and so forth. The naming service enables names to be defined and manipulated for objects, such as SID entities, contracts, and business processes. The registration service provides a management interface to add, modify, delete and browse objects. The contract location service enables searching based on attributes that have been defined for a contract.

Business View Interaction

A number of NGOSS artifacts represent business view interactions. These include:

- SID/eTOM mappings

- Use cases

- Sequence diagrams

- Business View contracts.

The iterative development of each of these artifacts represents the progressive detailing of the business view component of the interaction model. Each artifact enables the development of the next artifact in the list above.

While they are not contained strictly within the Technology-Neutral Architecture, the SID/eTOM mappings and use cases are both important in identifying and confirming technology-neutral contracts and components. Two other artifacts of the interaction architecture briefly mentioned above, contracts and components, are also discussed here as part of an an iterative approach to development.

SID/eTOM mappings represent the first interaction architecture artifact. Mappings currently exist for level 2 eTOM processes and level 1 SID Aggregate Business Entities. Figure 2.20 provides an example of these mappings for the SID/eTOM Product domain.

The **Product** Domain is concerned with the lifecycle of products and information and contract operations related to products' lifecycle. The Domain contains Aggregate Business Entities that deal with the strategic portfolio plans, products offered, product performance, product usage statistics, as well as the product instances delivered to a customer.

Product ABEs	Primary Vertical eTOM Process Groupings	Primary eTOM Level 2 Processes	Secondary eTOM Level 2 Processes
Product Specification Defines the functionality and characteristics of product offerings made available to the market.	M&OM – PLM	Product & Offer Development & Retirement	Product & Offer Capability Delivery
			Service Configuration & Activation
			SM&O Support & Readiness
Product Offering Represents tangible and intangible goods and services made available for a certain price to the market in the form of product catalogs. This ABE is also responsible for targeting market segments based on the appropriate market strategy.	M&OM – PLM	Product & Offer Development & Retirement	Marketing Fulfillment Response
			Product Marketing Communications & Promotion
			Product & Offer Capability Delivery
			Selling
			Order Handling
Product Represents an instance of a product offering subscribed to by a party, such as a customer, the place where the product is in use, as well as configuration characteristics, such as assigned telephone numbers and internet addresses. The Product ABE also tracks the services and/or resources through which the product is realized.	CRM – F	Order Handling	Selling
			Service Configuration & Activation
			Problem Handling
			Customer QoS/ SLA Management
			Billing & Collections Management
			Service Problem Management
			Service Quality Management
			Service & Specific Instance Rating
			SM&O Support & Readiness

Figure 2.20 – Partial SID/eTOM Product Domain Mapping

A primary eTOM level 2 process is responsible for managing the lifecycle of the information associated with a SID level 1 ABE. This means that the process creates instances of the entities that characterize the ABE and maintains the instances throughout the entities' time of interest to an enterprise. For example, the Product & Offer Development & Retirement process manages the lifecycle of the Product Specification ABE, the Product Offering ABE, their entities, as well as the level 2 SID ABEs, Product Offering Price, Product Offering Price Rules, Product Placement, and Product Promotion.

A secondary process uses instances of the entities that characterize the ABE.

Level 3 Product & Offer Development & Retirement processes are shown in Figure 2.21.

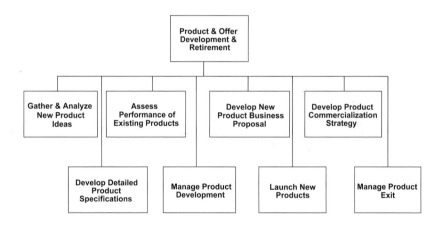

Figure 2.21 – Product & Offer Development & Retirement Level 3 Processes

Mapping of level 3 eTOM processes to ABEs at level 2 and business entities that make up level 1 ABEs is an effort that has just begun within the TM Forum at the time of this publication. Note: All Product Specification and Product Offering ABEs have not yet been identified. A potential mapping at this level is shown in Figure 2.22.

Product Offering ABEs/Entities to eTOM Level 3 Process Mappings	
SID ABE/Entities	**eTOM Level 3 Process (Primary)**
Product Specification ABE Entities	Gather & Analyze New Product Ideas
Product Offering ABE Entities	Develop Detailed Product Specifications; Manage Product Exit
Product Price ABE	Develop Detailed Product Specifications
Product Price Rule ABE	Develop Detailed Product Specifications
Product Placement ABE	Launch New Products; Manage Product Development
Product Promotion ABE	Launch New Products; Manage Product Development

Figure 2.22 – Product Specification and Offering ABE Mappings to eTOM Level 3 Processes

In Figure 2.22, primary processes create instances of entities that comprise the ABE.

SID to eTOM mappings are a useful tool for identifying and confirming

• Entities involved in use cases

• Entities (objects) involved in sequence diagrams

• Entities involved in contracts.

Use cases are the second of the four business view interaction architecture artifacts. While they primarily focus on the interaction between a user and a system, use cases also reference business entities. The first reference to business entities are in the name of the use case. eTOM level 3 are ideal candidates for use cases. In the table above the use case Develop Detailed Product Specifications, by its name acts on Product Specification entities and, most likely, Product Offering entities.

Detailed steps further define the use case and also reference business entities. For example, one step in the use case, Develop Detailed Product Specifications, may be: the user specifies the product offerings that makeup a product bundle. These two entities are manifested respectively in the SID model as SimpleProductOffering and BundledProductOffering. The text below shows a more complete example of the Develop Detailed Product Specification use case.

Develop Detailed Product Specification (basic flow)

1. The user (product manager) requests to create a bundled product offering (assumes product offering has already been created for simplicity of this example)

2. The system provides a method by which the user can search for a product offering or specify a particular product offering

3. The user provides details for the system to be able to conduct the search

4. The system provides a list of product offerings

5. The user selects the product offering to become the product offering bundle

6. The system provides a method by which the user can search for product offerings that will become part of the product offering bundle or specify the product offerings directly

7. The user provides details for the system to be able to conduct the search

8. The system provides a list of product offerings

9. The user selects the product offerings to become part of the product bundle

10. The system associates the product offerings with the product bundle

…the use case interaction continues…
The details of a use case are instrumental in constructing the third interaction artifact, sequence diagrams. Sequence diagrams depict the interaction among users (actors), such as a Product Manager in this example, and the entities (objects) that

are involved in the use case. For example, the Product Manager actor sends a message to the ProductOffering object requesting that a group of SimpleProductOfferings be grouped into a BundledProductOffering. A sequence diagram that represents the use case steps detailed above is shown in Figure 2.23.

Figure 2.23 – Partial Sequence Diagram for Develop Detailed Product Specifications

Business view contracts represent the fourth business view interaction model artifact. As such, contracts represent the culmination of business view interaction model artifacts. Contracts represent formal statements of the interaction contained within use cases and sequence diagrams. The information content of the messages, expressed in terms of SID entities and attributes define the details of inputs and outputs for a business view contract. In the Product Offering ABE example, a business view contract may include the processes (use cases) Develop Detailed Product Specifications, Manage Product Development, and Manage Product Exit. Business view contracts are currently under development by a number of NGOSS teams, including development of Order Fulfillment contracts by the eTOM team.

An NGOSS contract is a fundamental unit of interoperability in a system. It represents a specification of a service to be delivered. As mentioned in the previous paragraph, a business view contract formalizes the interaction (service delivered) as expressed by use cases and sequence diagrams. It is used to specify information and code necessary to implement the service.

A contract can express much more than the specification of a software interface. It may also define pre- and post-conditions, semantics for using the service, policies affecting the configuration, use, and operation of the service, and more. The contract specification covers the functional (such as associated business processes, associated use cases, and interaction points) and non-functional (such as regulatory limitations, assumptions, and stakeholders) characteristics and behavior of a service, along with its goal and obligations. Just as information and process architecture artifacts have their own lifecycle as they move through the four NGOSS views, contracts also have a similar lifecycle.

Additional details can be found in the Implementing Use Cases and Contracts section of the Implementing NGOSS chapter of this book.

System View Interaction

Development of system view interaction artifacts continues the transformation of some of the business view interaction model components. Three key artifacts form the basis of the interaction architecture within the system view. They are:

• Sequence diagrams

• System view contracts

• Components.

As in business view interaction, each artifact enables the development of the next artifact in the list above. Technology neutral components defined within the system view become a primary input to the implementation view, where technology specific characteristics are applied to them.

Sequence diagrams defined in the business view may be further decomposed if the associated use case is decomposed. For example, the use case (process) Develop Detailed Product Specifications may be further decomposed. A sample of this decomposition could be:

• Develop Bundled Product Offering

• Develop Product Offering Prices

• Specify Product Offering Price Rules.

Each of these use cases would have an accompanying sequence diagram and an accompanying system view contract. System view sequence diagrams are structured similarly to the business view sequence diagrams. System view contracts specify the architectural requirements necessary to design the contract, as defined by the business view. This is done in a technical, though technology-neutral manner appropriate for communication and understanding by someone who is part of a technical staff.

One key aspect of the NGOSS Technology-Neutral Architecture is the fact that it is component-based. A component is an independently deliverable set of software services expressed via system view contracts. For example, a Product Offering component provides services such as bundling product offerings and defining product offering prices. Each component is encapsulated and its interfaces manage access to the business rules, data, and operations.

A fully defined component is comprised of:

• A specification

• An interface

• An implementation (as part of the implementation view)

• Executables (as part of the deployment view).

A component's **specification** describes the data and processing aspects of a component as well as the rules and constraints that govern a component's behavior. The specification contains the contents of the business view and system view necessary for the development of a component. For example, the specification does not contain the use case or sequence diagrams, but does contain the detailed steps defined by the use cases and sequence diagrams. These steps, called operations, represent the functionality implemented in the application.

A component's **interface** describes how a user of a component interacts with it. For example, the driver's license number and national ID number are necessary to obtain a credit score for a mobile phone customer.

The **implementation** describes how the application will employ the component's specification. For example, what logic calculates a customer's credit score?

A component's **executable** (**deployment**), via the contracts it implements, deals with the physical aspects, such as the data base management language used and the physical platform on which the component executes.

The component characteristics described here increase the adaptability of the application layer for the enterprise by:

• Allowing each component to be developed and tested independently

• Enabling acquisition of components from internal or external sources

• Providing standards for interfaces that allow components to be easily "plugged" together

• Eliminating the need to start development of an application from scratch.

Chapter Three
Implementing NGOSS

This chapter provides a number of options for implementing NGOSS within an enterprise. One key point to remember is that the entire NGOSS program does not have to be implemented at once. NGOSS is not an all or nothing proposition. Nor does an enterprise have to implement the entire scope of one of NGOSS' elements. For example, an enterprise may wish to use the SID to jump start application development; the scope of an application development project may involve only the Customer domain. Or an enterprise may wish to add the model-driven architecture capabilities of the NGOSS Lifecycle.

Implementing the NGOSS Program

The key to implementing NGOSS was stated in the first chapter's section on becoming a lean operator. Adopting NGOSS means that an enterprise should consider the following steps:

• Decide that NGOSS is appropriate for your enterprise

• Assess where you are in relation to the NGOSS program

• Identify how to make the transition to NGOSS.

Making the Decision

The first step, making the decision, is really a question with only one answer today. The answer is "yes". When NGOSS was first introduced, the answer to the question was "maybe we'll wait" or "no". With the broad, industry-wide acceptance of NGOSS, an enterprise should no longer consider if NGOSS is appropriate, but rather when NGOSS will be adopted.

Assessing Where You Are

The second step is a bit more involved, but the later sections in this chapter address a number of ways in which NGOSS elements may be implemented. Briefly put, this step involves an enterprise assessing its use of comparable NGOSS elements, such as the eTOM and SID. An interdisciplinary team that includes both business stakeholders and application development stakeholders should undertake the assessment. A partial list of assessment questions is included in this section.

Questions are organized using the main NGOSS elements:

• NGOSS Lifecycle

• eTOM

- SID

- Technology-Neutral Architecture (Interaction Architecture).

These questions are important when making a decision on what aspects of NGOSS are to be implemented within an enterprise. As you read this chapter keep these questions in mind.

When considering the implementation of the NGOSS Lifecycle evaluate:

- The degree to which your current development process includes the views, and SANRR methodology?

- Is it important to include the perspectives within your development environment?

    - Which perspectives are important and why?

    - Which perspectives are not important and why not?

- Does your organization employ a method for analyzing process-oriented challenges, such as process redesign?

When considering the implementation of the eTOM ask:

- Does your organization employ a process model?

    - If so, what are the perceived benefits from employing the eTOM or mapping the current process model to the eTOM?

    - If not, are there any perceived disadvantages associated with employing an industry standard process model?

- Are there any areas of the eTOM that are of particular importance to your organization?

- Can existing eTOM process flows assist in gaining a better understanding of your processes?

- Are you undertaking or planning to undertake any new development projects?

- Are you considering a "fresh look" at the processes within your organization?

- What groups within your organization would employ a model such as eTOM?

- Are tools in place to support a process model that can be managed by various groups within your organization?

When considering the implementation of the SID ask:

- Does your organization employ a shared information model?

  - Do you see any benefits to employing a shared information model?

  - Do you see any disadvantages to employing a shared information model?

- Are there integration issues with internal or externally developed applications?

- Are there any partnerships with other enterprises envisioned?

- Are you undertaking or planning to undertake any new development projects?

- What groups within your organization would employ a shared information model?

- Are tool(s) in place to manage a shared information model across various groups within your organization?

When considering the implementation of the Technology-Neutral Architecture (Interaction Architecture) ask:

- Does your organization employ models to scope a project?

  - Do you see any benefits to employing a model to scope projects?

  - Do you see any disadvantages to employing a model to scope projects?

- Does your organization employ use cases?

- Does your organization employ sequence diagrams?

- Does your organization employ application design specifications?

- Are tool(s) in place to manage the artifacts of an interaction architecture?

- Do you separate business process logic from component implementation?

- Do your applications employ a common security infrastructure?

- Do you employ policies or some form of rules engine that enable users to specify business rules?

- How are components managed and located within your deployed applications?

Transitioning to NGOSS

With the results of the assessment in hand, the next step is making the transition to employing NGOSS within your enterprise. The answers to the assessment questions can help prioritize which aspects of NGOSS are included in your implementation.

If you are satisfied that your current development process meets the needs of your organization, the SANRR methodology may be left out of your implementation plans. However, if a model-driven approach is of interest, then consider using those parts of the NGOSS Lifecycle, such as the views, SANRR and perspectives, that support a model-driven approach.

If new application development is a priority, then you should consider the use of the eTOM, SID, and Technology-Neutral Architecture in your NGOSS implementation plans. This chapter describes a number of ways in which these artifacts can be used to support the development of new applications. This support includes assistance with scoping projects and providing industry standard frameworks (the eTOM and SID) with which to get a development project off to a quick start.

When acquiring applications that must integrate with your enterprise's applications, or interfacing with partners' applications, then SID can be used as part of an application integration framework.

These and other uses of NGOSS artifacts described in this chapter will help you decide how to transition to NGOSS, which artifacts to use, and how to use them.

NGOSS Program Stakeholders

The type of stakeholder making the transition also impacts the use of NGOSS artifacts. Stakeholders wishing to implement the NGOSS program include service providers, equipment vendors, independent software vendors, and system integrators. These stakeholders can be divided into two categories:

• Stakeholders that deliver products, either directly or indirectly, to consumers (product delivery stakeholders)

• Stakeholders that support those that deliver products (product delivery support stakeholders).

Stakeholders in the first category can include service providers, ISV's and equipment vendors. Stakeholders in the second category can include equipment vendors and system integrators.

Both categories have the opportunity to implement all or some of NGOSS' elements, such as the SID, the eTOM, the Technology-Neutral Architecture, and the NGOSS Lifecycle. One major difference between the two stakeholder categories is the way in which the eTOM is employed within their enterprises.

Implementing the NGOSS Lifecycle

Implementing NGOSS does not mean that an organization should discontinue use of its current application development process. However, if your organization is considering adopting a new approach to application development, then the NGOSS Lifecycle should be considered for use. Additionally, if your current development process is lacking in certain areas, such as process modeling and models, then those NGOSS Lifecycle artifacts that fill the missing gaps should be investigated for use. Or, if your organization is looking for a simple problem solving process, the SANRR method could be used.

This book does not presume to offer complete guidance on adopting a new application development process. Volumes of books have already been written on this subject. What is presented here is how and why the various aspects of the NGOSS Lifecycle can be put to use within your organization.

For example, a development process should accommodate service provider and service developer perspectives. These views ensure that all those involved in the development of an application can understand the application within their own context. A service developer may also be interested in the service provider perspective. The four views, business, system, implementation, and deployment, should be present within a development process. That is not to say that each view needs to be maintained. Often, an organization will maintain a logical perspective that consists of the business view transformed into a system view, and the two physical perspective represented by the implementation and deployment views.

Alternatively, the business, system, and implementation view may be combined into a single view, or model. However, this may not be the preferred choice when using model-driven development. In this case, a separation between the logical and physical perspectives is important to enable multiple physical perspectives to be generated from a single logical view. Keeping a separate business view and system view is left up to the NGOSS implementer, and can be decided based upon how much it costs to maintain a separation between these two views.

A key point to make here is that the development process should proceed from the business view through to the deployment view when developing new applications. When analyzing existing applications, it may be useful to reverse engineer a deployed view into some number of the other views in order to separate the concerns covered by each view.

Use cases and contracts, also key members of the NGOSS Lifecycle, should receive serious consideration for implementation. Their implementation is discussed in the Implementing the Technology-Neutral Architecture section of this chapter.

Implementing eTOM

The eTOM is now known as the de jure telecommunications industry standard process framework and there are a wide range of uses of the eTOM in the lean and adaptive enterprise. Organizations across the world have deployed eTOM as a tool for cataloging their telecom and enterprise processes, as a tool for developing operational process flows, as a requirements capture framework; and as a tool for mapping organization responsibilities. This section provides an overview of the techniques and rationales associated with some of these approaches.

Levels of Process Maturity in Organizations

There is a common misconception that eTOM is most useful to organizations that have little or no formal processes. While eTOM provides help and structure to such organizations, it is to the well-structured organization that eTOM provides the greatest initial advantage. Three levels of organization can benefit by implementing eTOM:

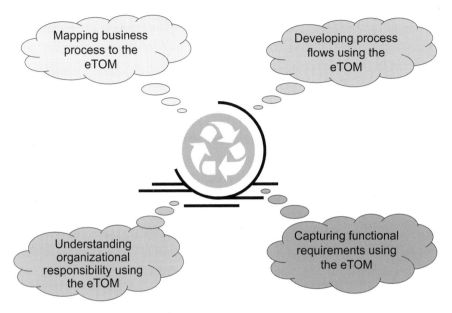

Figure 3.1 – eTOM Uses

Process Immature

Immature organizations have a very loose set of processes that are used to control and drive their mission critical operations. These processes vary widely across different business units, using different approaches and different terminology to describe the same things. Mission critical processes often depend on 'heroes' who understand the 'way things get done' to ensure the smooth operation of the organization. There is generally no end-to-end process owner for any of the key processes and there are typically loose hand-off points between the various process stages as the process responsibility moves from one business unit to the next.

Process Aware

Process Aware organizations have an awareness of the need to manage processes end to end. Processes are typically well documented in a standard template, although use of terminology varies from process to process. There may be an organization wide process framework but much of the organization may be unaware of the existence of this framework.

Process Centric

A process centric organization will have a well-defined set of operational processes for all mission critical business areas, each mapped to an organization wide process framework. Processes will be documented to a common template, using a common dictionary of terminology to describe the process. Each key process will have an end-to-end process owner or else clearly defined ownership handover points between process stages with clearly defined escalation procedures to resolve conflict. Process performance will be measured end to end and responsibility for process performance will rest with board level executives.

Mapping Existing Processes into the Standard eTOM Framework

Regardless of the process maturity of an organization, a key first step in implementing the eTOM is to map the existing processes into the standard framework. Until this step is carried out it is very difficult for the organization to see how the wealth of material existing in the eTOM can be of benefit to their organization. For example, once this mapping is complete the organization can employ a common language regarding its requirements to its suppliers that is globally adopted, thus avoiding costly miscommunications. The organization can also choose to adopt the pre-existing process definitions (and in limited cases process flows) that are defined in the eTOM in areas that the organization has not yet developed formal processes. The difficulty of performing this task will vary depending on the organizational maturity and the scope of activity defined in each process.

The first step in this process is to gather all of the existing process information across the organization. In a process-centric or process aware organization this may be possible to do as a single organization wide activity. In a process immature organization this will need to be done in a number of separate initiatives, with a process model owner being nominated to pull together the disparate information into a single organization wide model.

Mapping current processes to the eTOM framework involves three steps:

Step 1: Evaluate the level of process maturity across the organization and define a plan for mapping the processes to the eTOM framework dividing the organization into appropriate number of business units for the mapping purpose. It is essential that all of the key process architects be available for the mapping exercise to rapidly resolve questions regarding any ambiguity regarding the scope of certain processes. It is also essential that a process architect experienced in the structure and intent of the eTOM facilitates the session.

Process Number	Key Processes
1	Customer Care
2	Order Taking
3	Fault Management
4	Provisioning & Activation
5	Performance Management
6	Billing
7	Inventory Management
8	Network Introduction

Figure 3.2- Organization X High Level Processes

Step 2: Write down all of the key organisational processes, an example of this is shown in figure 3.2, and do a first pass high-level mapping to a level 2 eTOM diagram. An example of this is shown in Figure 3.3.

It is a very quick process to map these processes onto a level 2 eTOM in a visual fashion as shown in Figure 3.3. This need not be a rigorous mapping and some of the details will certainly change as a more detailed level 3 mapping is performed.

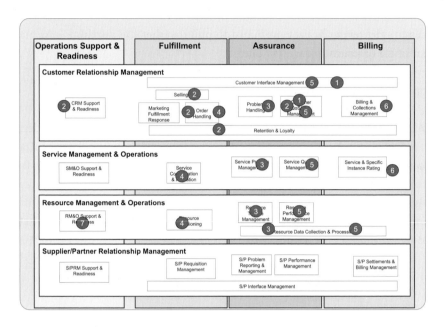

Operations Support & Readiness	Fulfillment	Assurance	Billing

Customer Relationship Management

Customer Interface Management ⑤ ①

Selling ②

CRM Support & Readiness ②

Marketing Fulfillment Response

Order Handling ② ④

Problem Handling ③

Billing & Collections Management ⑥

Retention & Loyalty ②

Service Management & Operations

SM&O Support & Readiness

Service Configuration & Activation ④

Service Problem Management ③

Service Quality Management ⑤

Service & Specific Instance Rating ⑥

Resource Management & Operations

RM&O Support & Readiness ⑦

Resource Provisioning ④

Resource Trouble Management ③

Resource Performance Management ⑤

Resource Data Collection & Processing ③ ⑤

Supplier/Partner Relationship Management

S/PRM Support & Readiness

S/P Requisition Management

S/P Problem Reporting & Management

S/P Performance Management

S/P Settlements & Billing Management

S/P Interface Management

Figure 3.3 - Current Process to eTOM Process Mapping

In this example there is a reward of valuable information.

First, it highlights areas where the defined processes are at too coarse a level. Process 6 (Billing) covers both the invoicing and rating eTOM level 2 processes. Likewise, Process 3 (Fault Management) and Process 5 (Performance Management) cover a range of level 2 processes across three separate process functional groupings.

Second, it identifies areas where multiple processes refer to the same level 2 process. This is the case in the Resource Data Collection and Processing level 2 process, which is referred to by both the Fault management and the Performance management current processes.

Third, it rapidly identifies gaps where there are no identifiable processes. Notably the whole Supplier/Partner process horizontal has no processes mapped to it. This may not be a cause of concern as there may be very simple supplier/partner dealings. However, it may also point to a gap where key activities of the organization are exposed to risk due to poorly defined or missing processes.

Finally, it identifies areas where there are orphan processes, which have no specific eTOM supporting processes and as such are not being properly exploited. Process 8 (Network Introduction) is one case in point.

Step 3: This step involves taking this mapping to the next stage of detail. Where there is insufficient detail in the current processes then this is a difficult task to achieve. However, in most cases additional detail can be extracted from the high level processes. In this example, the high level processes have distinct steps or phases, many of which can be mapped to eTOM level 3 processes. An example of this is shown in Figure 3.4.

Process Number	Key Processes for Company X	eTOM Level 2 Processes	Included Level 3 Processes
1	Customer Care	Customer Interface Management	Manage Contact
			Manage Request (including Self Service)
		Customer QoS/SLA Management	Manage QoS/SLA Violation
2	Order Taking	Customer QoS/SLA Management	
		Order Handling	
		Loyalty & Retention	

Figure 3.4 - Detailed Process Mapping

The Company X process called Customer Care maps reasonably well to the eTOM Level 2 processes Customer Interface Management and Customer QoS/SLA Management. The details of the Customer Care Processes indicate that it relates to the activities surrounding dealing with customers, namely managing the contact, managing requests and managing QoS/SLA violations. It is also discovered that there are aspects of Customer Interface Management and Customer QoS/SLA Management that are not covered in the Customer Care process. For example, it does not address the activities surrounding analyzing the performance of the customer interface. Further work would eventually show that these activities are covered in the process which Company X calls 'Performance Management'.

By doing this next level of analysis a company is able to identify new ways of grouping sub-activities of existing processes into new processes, which align better to the eTOM structure. Another benefit of this is that a clear mapping table can be generated which allows a translation from formal eTOM process names to current proprietary process names. In the long run it would be recommended to align the process names fully. However, this is not necessary in the early stages of mapping.

Mapping Process Flows using the eTOM

Once an organization has mapped their business process definitions to the eTOM they now have the ability to begin using their process map as the building blocks for the development of process flows.

The general approach to be adopted follows the following methodology:

- Identify the general process interaction

- Map the detailed level 2 process interactions

- Map the detailed level 2 process flow (using a swim lane approach)

- Examine the level 3 decompositions to identify further interactions and flows .

In this example the introduction of a DSL service is planned.

Step 1: Identify the general process interaction surrounding the business process to be defined. Sketch the expected high-level interactions on a level 2 eTOM diagram to accomplish this step (Figure 3.5).

This high level interaction shows the main processes that will be impacted in the context of DSL Fulfillment. It may not be accurate at this stage but provides the basis upon which step 2 can be carried out. By examining this high-level interaction diagram three process threads can be identified.

- Pre-Sale activities (Figure 3.6)

- Ordering activities (Figure 3.7)

- Post-Order activities (Figure 3.8)

Step 2: Map the detailed level 2 process interactions against the three process threads identified. To do this a more formal process interaction diagram is adopted which places each of the level 2 processes in their respective positions in the eTOM level 2 diagram and in their respective functional groupings. At this level there is no concept of chronological flow introduced. The focus is merely to define the necessary interactions to the next level of detail.

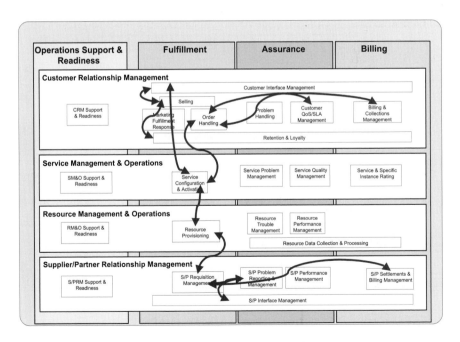

Figure 3.5 DSL Fulfillment High Level Interations

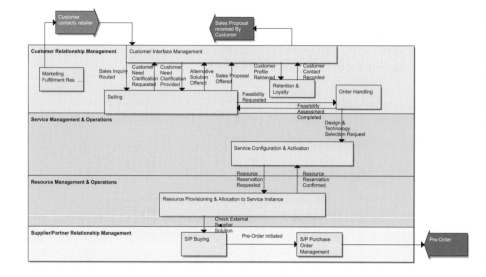

Figure 3.6 - Pre-Sale Level 2 Processes

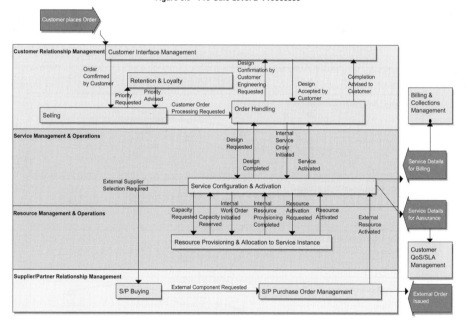

Figure 3.7 Ordering Level 2 Processes

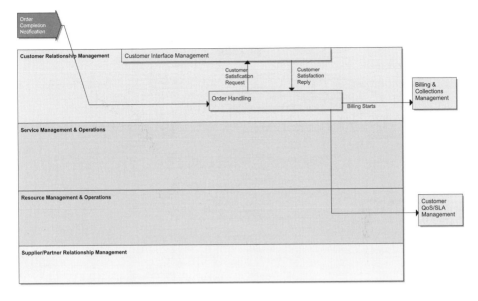

Figure 3.8 - Post Order Level 2 Processes

Step 3: Map the detailed level 2 process flows. This is only shown in Figure 3.9 for the pre-sale process. The same approach is used for both the ordering and post-sale process. The critical difference from the previous diagrams is that chronological order is introduced here and the diagram clearly identifies which process steps must happen prior to other process steps.

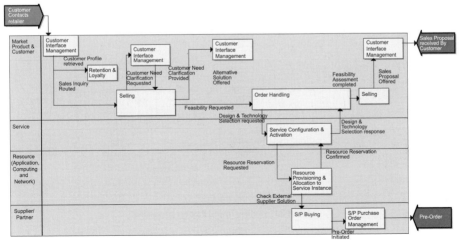

Figure 3.9 – Pre-Sale Dynamic Order Process Flow

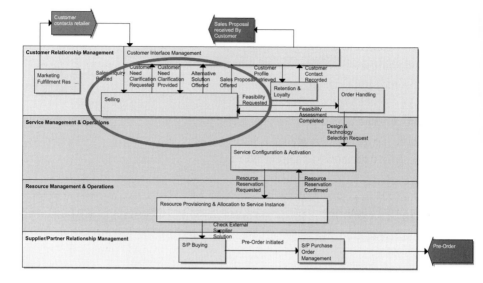

Figure 3.10 Pre-Sale Level 2 Process Interaction - Highlighting Selling Process

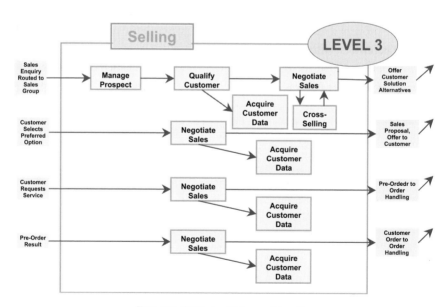

Figure 3.11 - Selling Level 3 Process Interaction

Step 4: In all but the simplest organizations a level 2 process flow will not be sufficiently detailed to allow business activities to be carried out. So several further levels of detail may be required to define a process that can be implemented by operations and support staff.

Taking the pre-sale level 2 process flow and delving into further detail as shown in Figure 3.10, shows that the selling process is too high level and a further level of detail is required as shown in Figure 3.11.

This level of detail may be sufficient in some organizations to allow operations and support staff to implement the process. More likely a further level of detail needs to be defined before the process is at the appropriate level of detail for the organization.

The eTOM as a Requirements Gathering Framework

There are many software implementation methodologies, which espouse either a less formal or more formal approach to requirements gathering. However, it is fair to say that regardless of whether you favor extreme programming approaches or its more formal cousins, the first step is to go through a requirements gathering phase to rapidly and accurately understand what is needed. The eTOM is an effective tool to help address the challenge of effectively capturing business requirements and ensuring the accurate linkage of these requirements to the business processes.

An example of the requirements for a new feature is shown in Figure 3.12. The implementation of a new set of capabilities surrounding the user interface presented to the customer service agents is in progress. The feature is called "enhanced customer management user views".

Feature Number	Feature Name	High Level Requirements
EN84-02-05	Enhanced Customer Management User views	this feature is an enhancement to allow the customer service agent to view customer billing and service details in a single user view. It will also allow the users to view all open service problems relating to a customer including status and any actions taken.

Figure 3.12 – eTOM and Requirements Gathering

The first step involves mapping the existing high-level requirements to the level 1 and 2 processes of the eTOM. Due to its enterprise coverage breadth, its operational focus and its formalized decomposition structure, eTOM provides a framework for capturing high level and detailed functional requirements.

Feature Number	Feature Name	High Level Requirements	eTOM level 1 Processes	Affected eTOM Level 2 Processes
EN84-02-05	Enhanced Customer Management User views	This feature is an enhancement to allow the customer service agent to view customer billing and service details in a single user view. It will also allow the users to view all open service problems relating to a customer including status and any action taken.	Customer Relationship Management	Customer Interface Management
				Customer QoS/SLA Management

Figure 3.13 – Mapping Requirements to eTOM Processes

Further levels of decomposition allow the requirement to be broken down into further constituent parts, each part of the requirement being mapped to specific level 3 eTOM processes.

Feature Number	Feature Name	eTOM level 1 Processes	Affected eTOM Level 2 Processes	Affected eTOM Level 3 Processes	Detailed functional requirements
EN84-02-05	Enhanced Customer Management User views	Customer Relationship Management	Customer Interface Management	Manage contact	This feature will involve............
				Manage Request	This feature will involve............
				Analyze & report on Customer	This feature will involve............
			Customer QoS/SLA Management	Assess Customer SLA/QoS performance	This feature will involve............
				Manage QoS/SLA Violation	This feature will involve............
				Manage Reporting	This feature will involve............

Figure 3.14 – Requirements Mapped to Level 3 Processes

This approach captures the explicit linkage between the processes within the eTOM framework for the business area concerned and the IT components, which provide the automated solution for the business requirements. If this information is stored in an enterprise architecture repository it can provide the reference base for answering questions such as:

• Does automation for this function already exist

• Are there any opportunities to reduce duplication.

Mapping Organizational Responsibilities

Large organizations, by their very nature, suffer difficulties in clearly defining the responsibility boundaries between different business areas. In a typical scenario many stakeholders in the organization would claim to have responsibility for the same area of business. This can lead to conflict and in many cases poor delivery performance. The eTOM can help an organization gain perspective on responsibility by focusing individuals on clearly defining ownership of the business processes as opposed to the business roles.

An example of how the eTOM is used to help define organizational responsibility follows.

There are four key individuals who have conflicting views over who has ownership of key areas such as Customer Interface Management.

Customer Care Manager: responsible for all aspects of how the enterprise relates directly to the end customer.

Product Development Manager: responsible for all aspects of the product development and delivery up to launch.

Product Manager: responsible for all aspects of the product from cradle to grave and for the product profitability.

Marketing Manager: responsible for the overall marketing message and development of the sales collateral.

A number of people in this organization believe they have 'total' responsibility for the product and as such this can lead to conflict and poor performance.

The eTOM can help as part of a methodology to help resolve this confusion.

Step 1: Collect all involved individuals in a workshop with eTOM knowledgeable facilitators. Work with the participants to map out their areas of accountability on an eTOM chart.

Start with eTOM level 2 (shown in Figure 3.15) as this will give a very good high level first pass impression.

Step 2: Identify the areas of overlap and under-lap across the organization as shown in Figure 3.16.

For the overlapping areas expand to level 3 processes in an attempt to resolve overlap. For the areas of under-lap it will be necessary to confirm that other managers have clear responsibility over those areas.

Step 3: Identify the areas of overlap and under-lap across the organization.

This should help in resolving much of the overlap but it is to be expected that there will continue to be areas of overlap. In this scenario consider using an accountability mapping tool such as RACI to clearly identify actual accountabilities.

R = Responsible

A = Accountable

C = Consult

I = Inform

RACI is widely used in many business scenarios. The *Responsible* individual is the person who is recognized as the person doing the work. The *Accountable* person has the ultimate authority to approve the work and will be held responsible if the work doesn't get done. The *Consult* person has an opinion, which should be taken into account regarding the work but has no veto power. The *Inform* person is simply someone who needs to know that the work is being done or has been done

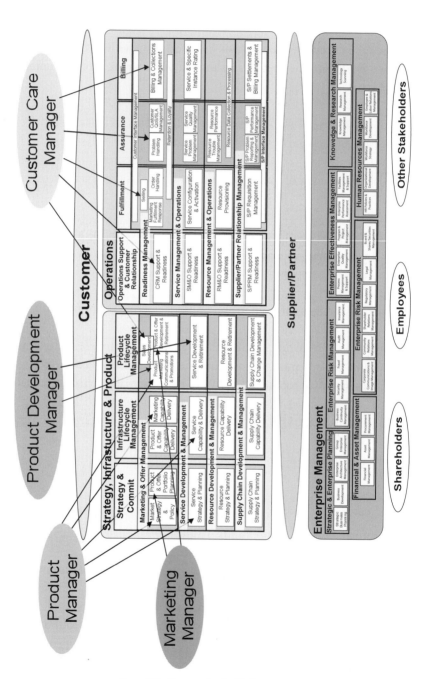

Figure 3.15 – Managers Involved in Processes

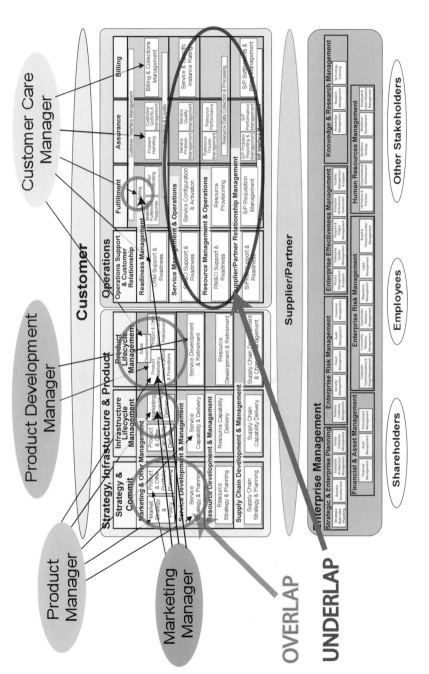

Figure 3.16 – Overlapping/Underlapping areasa of Responsibity

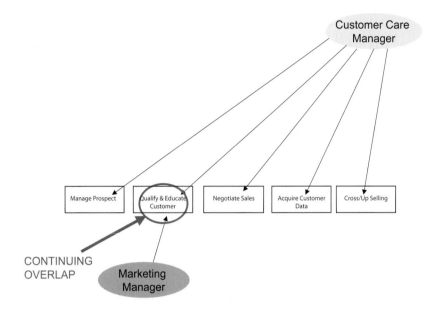

Figure 3.17 - Organizational Overlap/Under-lap

eTOM level 1 Processes	eTOM Level 2 Processes	eTOM Level 3 Processes	Product Manager	Development Manager	Marketing Manager	Customer Care Manager
Customer Relationship Management	Selling	Manage prospect	I	-		R/A
		Qualify and Educate Customer	I	-	C	R/A
		Negotiate Sales	I	-		R/A
		Acquire Customer Data	I	-		R/A
		Cross/Up Selling	I	-	C	R/A
		Manage Reporting	I	-		R/A

Figure 3.18 - RACI Matrix

Using the RACI framework it is possible to resolve ownership conflict issues by identifying that while all parties may have a role to play in common process areas and have a need to be informed or consulted, there is only one person who has responsibility or accountability in each key process area.

Implementing the SID

Upon its introduction as an NGOSS deliverable, some NGOSS implementers thought that using the SID would mean that their applications' internal data structures would have to be changed to reflect conformance with the SID. This is not the case! Besides providing a vocabulary for common information concepts, the SID Framework, the SID model, and its contents can be put to a number of uses within an enterprise.

Potential SID uses include:

• Employing the SID as part of an application integration framework (SID UML model and XML schema)

• Focusing new/enhanced application development on the SID Framework, model, and addenda

• Using the SID Framework to organize current information models

• Evaluating conformance to the SID using TM Forum compliance program criteria

• Evaluating potential application acquisitions and (potential) partner applications using SID TM Forum compliance program criteria

• Using the SID Framework to organize use cases

SID as Part of an Application Integration Framework

Enterprises with an embedded software application base sometimes include migrating existing databases to a SID-like structure as part of a migration strategy. This strategy is not necessary from an application interoperability perspective. One key to SID conformance from an interoperability perspective is to expose an application's data using API's with a SID-like structure. This section provides an overview of how to use the SID as part of an application integration framework. Figure 3.19 shows three key steps when using the SID as part of an application integration strategy.

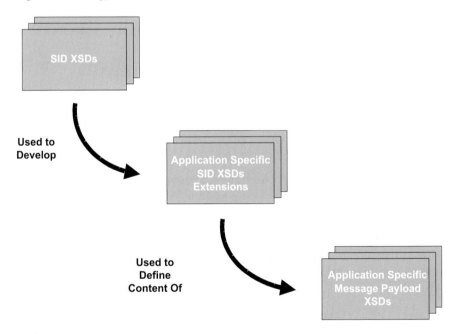

Figure 3.19 – SID Within an Application Integration Framework

The first step is to adopt the SID XML schema (Xsds) and use them to develop application-specific XSDs. An example of a fragment of the SID Party entity XSD is shown in Figure 3.20. The figure shows the Party entity and its attributes along with a LanguageAbility entity (and its attributes) a Party may possess and the Language (and its attributes) to which the LanguageAbility pertains.

```
<xs:complexType name="Party" mixed="false">
        <xs:sequence>
                <xs:element name="partyId" minOccurs="0"/>
                <xs:element name="validFor" type="SIDBusCm:TimePeriod" minOccurs="0"/>
                <xs:element name="LanguageAbility" minOccurs="0"/>
                <xs:element name="PartyRole" minOccurs="0"/>
        </xs:sequence>
</xs:complexType>
<xs:complexType name="LanguageAbility" mixed="false">
        <xs:sequence>
                <xs:element name="readingProficiency" minOccurs="0"/>
                <xs:element name="writingProficiency" minOccurs="0"/>
                <xs:element name="speakingProficiency" minOccurs="0"/>
                <xs:element name="listeningProficiency" minOccurs="0"/>
                <xs:element name="Language" minOccurs="0"/>
                <xs:element name="Party" minOccurs="0"/>
        </xs:sequence>
</xs:complexType>
<xs:complexType name="Language" mixed="false">
        <xs:sequence>
                <xs:element name="alphabetName" minOccurs="0"/>
                <xs:element name="dialectNames" minOccurs="0"/>
                <xs:element name="OfficiallyUsedInCountry" minOccurs="0"/>
                <xs:element name="DefinesPartyName" minOccurs="0"/>
                <xs:element name="AbilityInLanguage" minOccurs="0"/>
                <xs:element name="UsedToExpressPartyIdentification" minOccurs="0"/>
        </xs:sequence>
</xs:complexType>
```

Figure 3.20 – SID Party XSD Example

Notice that all elements are specified as nillable with a minimum number of
occurrences of zero, which means that an entity's attributes and associations are
optional from a value and presence perspective. This may be in opposition to an
entity's attributes and associations within the SID model. The reason for this will
become clearer when message payloads are discussed. The optional characteristics
of attributes and associations can be changed when defining message payloads as
will be described later in this section.

The SID is a framework model, and, as such, extending the SID is expected. The next step is to use the SID to develop application-specific extensions to it. Figure 3.21 provides an example of an extension to the SID Party XSD.

```
<xs:complexType name="Party">
        <xs:complexContent>
                <xs:extension base="SIDBusCm:Party">
                        <xs:sequence>
                                <xs:element name="ApplicationSpecificExtensions"/>
                        </xs:sequence>
                </xs:extension>
        </xs:complexContent>
</xs:complexType>
<xs:complexType name="LanguageAbility">
        <xs:complexContent>
                <xs:extension base="SIDBusCm:LanguageAbility">
                        <xs:sequence>
                                <xs:element name="ApplicationSpecificExtensions"/>
                        </xs:sequence>
                </xs:extension>
        </xs:complexContent>
</xs:complexType>
<xs:complexType name="Language">
        <xs:complexContent>
                <xs:extension base="SIDBusCm:Language">
                        <xs:sequence>
                                <xs:element name="ApplicationSpecificExtensions"/>
                        </xs:sequence>
                </xs:extension>
        </xs:complexContent>
</xs:complexType>
```

Figure 3.21 – Application Specific SID XSD Extension

Notice that the XML "extension" attribute is used to include the SID entity within the application specific extension. The SID XSDs should not be changed to develop application specific extensions. If a future release of SID XSDs is desired to be used, these extensions would have to be reapplied. However, a restriction base of SID entities can be used to define another set of SID-like schema that are devoid of un-needed (by an application) attributes and associations.

A restriction base provides a copy of attributes from the base entity (in this example, Party). Unnecessary attributes and associations can be deleted and the types of remaining attributes and association can be further restricted from those in the base entity. For example, an attribute whose minimum number of occurrences is zero in the base can be changed to one (to make it mandatory) in the application specific extension entity that restricts the base entity. For example, the Party attribute validFor could be made mandatory in the application specific extension. W3C.org provides more information on the use of extension and restriction bases.

```
<xs:element name="CreateParty">
        <xs:complexType>
                <xs:sequence>
                        <xs:element name="Party" type="AppOpsCm:CreateParty"/>
                </xs:sequence>
        </xs:complexType>
</xs:element>
<xs:complexType name="CreateParty">
        <xs:complexContent>
                <xs:restriction base="AppSIDBusCm:Party">
                        <xs:sequence>
                                <xs:sequence>
                                        <xs:element name="partyId" type="xs:string"
nillable="false"/>
                                        <xs:element name="validFor" type="SIDBusCm:TimePeriod"
nillable="false"/>
                                        <xs:element name="LanguageAbility" type="AppOpsCm:Crea
tePartyLanguageAbility" nillable="false" maxOccurs="unbounded"/>
                                </xs:sequence>
                                <xs:sequence>
                                        <xs:element name="ApplicationSpecificExtensions"/>
                                </xs:sequence>
                        </xs:sequence>
                </xs:restriction>
        </xs:complexContent>
</xs:complexType>
<xs:complexType name="CreatePartyLanguageAbility">
        <xs:complexContent>
                <xs:restriction base="AppSIDBusCm:LanguageAbility">
                        <xs:sequence>
                                <xs:sequence>
                                        <xs:element name="readingProficiency" type="xs:string"
nillable="true" minOccurs="0"/>
                                        <xs:element name="writingProficiency" type="xs:string"
nillable="true" minOccurs="0"/>
                                        <xs:element name="speakingProficiency" type="xs:string"
nillable="true" minOccurs="0"/>
                                        <xs:element name="listeningProficiency" type="xs:
string" nillable="true" minOccurs="0"/>
                                        <xs:element name="Language" type="xs:string"
nillable="true"/>
                                </xs:sequence>
                                <xs:sequence>
                                        <xs:element name="ApplicationSpecificExtensions"
nillable="true" minOccurs="0"/>
```

Figure 3.22 – Message Payload XSD Using Application Specific SID Extension XSDs

The third step is to use the application specific SID XSD extensions to form the basis for API message payloads as shown in Figure 3.22.

The message payloads use the extended SID XSDs as an XML restriction base. This allows attributes and associations to be further restricted from their full optionality defined in the original SID XSDs. For example, in the sample XSD above the partyID and validFor attributes have been changed to required (minimum occurrences equals one) and there is a requirement for at least one LanguageAbility. This is because the operation that creates a Party requires values for partyID, validFor, and at least one LanguageAbility to be present.

Focusing New/Enhanced Development on the SID

When an enterprise takes on a project to enhance an existing application or to (re-)develop an application, considering the use of the SID Framework, model, and addendum within the project provides an opportunity to get a rather large head-start. Other benefits include using a de-facto industry standard framework, model, and its included information-related vocabulary. Employing the SID in this manner reduces the cost of interoperability when interfacing/integrating with other SID-based applications.

The entire SID model does not have to be used for a project, although it should be considered for use as a unifying model for all projects as described in a later section of this chapter. A review of SID Framework domains is a first step in defining the scope of the SID to use within a project. Figure 3.23 depicts the SID Framework's Domains.

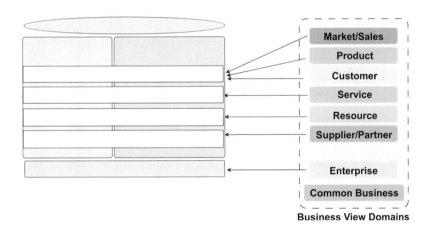

Business View Domains

Figure 3.23 – SID Domains

The SID framework is partitioned into a number of domains, which are primarily aligned with the business interests of the enterprise. Each domain contains information highly cohesive to the domain. A Common Business Entities domain contains information categories common across domains.

The next step is to identify which contents of domains within the scope of the project should be included. Each domain is comprised of a set of Aggregate Business Entities (ABE). An ABE is a cohesive set of related entities such as Customer, CustomerAccount, CustomerAccountContact and so forth that make up the Customer ABE within the Customer domain. The scope of the project is further defined by including the associated ABEs. A description of SID domains and ABEs can be found in GB922 SID Concepts and Principles. Figure 3.24 depicts the complete SID Framework of domains and ABEs.

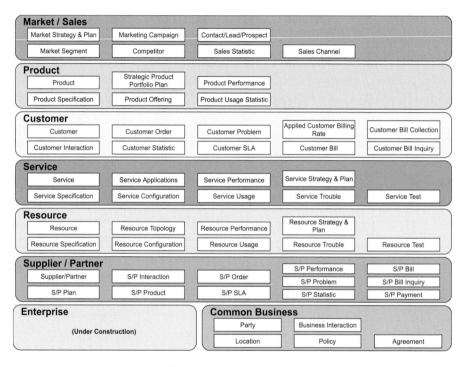

Figure 3.24 – SID Framework of Domains and ABEs

The third step is to create a copy of the SID model or create a model from scratch. Figure 3.25 depicts the package structure.

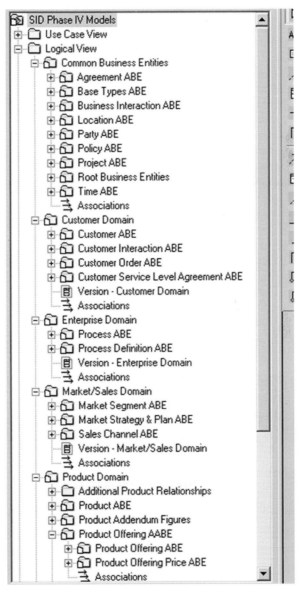

Figure 3.25 – SID Package Structure

The final step, which is repeated as needed, is to add application specific extensions to the SID-based model. Figure 3.26 depicts an example of a SID extension.

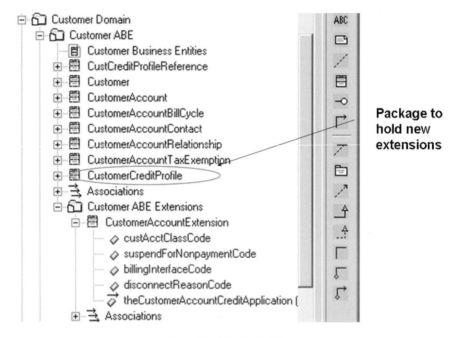

Figure 3.26 – Extending the SID

A new package is added to hold the extensions so that future versions of the Customer ABE can be incorporated into the model. If the extensions were added directly to the Customer ABE package, updating the model to include a new version of the SID Customer ABE would remove the application specific extensions.

Adding Attributes

Attributes should not be added directly to SID model business entities or business entity subclasses. Rather, create a subclass of the SID model business entity to which the attributes will be added. The subclass will inherit all of the attributes and associations from the SID business entity thus maintaining the integrity of the SID model. The new subclass holds the attributes as shown in Figure 3.27.

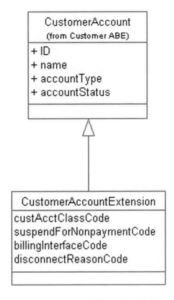

Figure 3.27 – Extending a SID Business Entity

The name of the business entity, CustomerAccountExtension, that holds attribute extensions is the name recommended by the SID Model team. An alternate name is CustomerAccountSpecialization, since a subclass is used to hold the attributes. The actual name is at the discretion of the individual extending the SID model. At a minimum, a consistent naming convention should be used.

A subclass is added to hold the extensions so that future versions of the Customer ABE and Customer entity can be incorporated into the model. If the extensions were added directly to the Customer entity, updating the model to include a new version of the SID Customer entity would remove the application specific extensions.

Adding entities

As in adding attributes, new entities should not be added directly to an existing SID ABE package, but rather added to the package that holds the SID model ABE extensions.

One of the techniques is used when attributes as well as a new class need to be added to the SID to extend an existing SID class. In the example below, the new entity (CustomerAccountCreditApplication) needs to be related to an extension of the existing SID CustomerAccount entity (CustomerAccountExtension). First, the existing SID entity (creating CustomerAccountExtension) is sub-classed. Next, an association (CreditApplicationSubmittedBy) is defined between the subclass of the existing SID entity and the new entity. Figure 3.28 shows an example of using this technique.

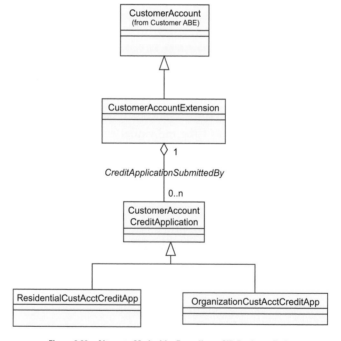

Figure 3.28 – Alternate Method for Extending a SID Business Entity

Patterns For Defining New Aggregate Business Entities

These guidelines should be used when developing a new ABE. Occasionally they may be used when adding more detail to an existing ABE. The guidelines include:

- Business entity patterns

- Association, attribute, and package naming conventions

- Guidelines for naming entities

- Guidelines for defining association classes vs. simple associations.

Business Entity Patterns are described here. The other guidelines can be found in the SID addendum GB922U - Using the SID

Business Entity Patterns

There are established sets of business entity patterns that are used in the SID. These include:

- Entity Specification/Entity

- Entity/Entity Role

- Composite/Component

- Entity Characteristic Spec/Entity Characteristic.

The Entity Specification/Entity pattern is described here.

Entity Specification/Entity Pattern

The Entity Specification/Entity pattern is used throughout the SID model. Typically, most core business entities (that is, an entity within an ABE that is not dependent upon any other entity within the ABE, such as Customer, Product, Service) have their invariant attributes, methods, relationships and constraints defined by a specification, such as Product Specification and Service Specification. Customer does not have a related specification entity at this time.

This pattern should not be applied to existing ABEs, but should receive high consideration when adding a new ABE or detailing an existing ABE that has not been developed. Figure 3.29 shows the use of this pattern in the Root ABE.

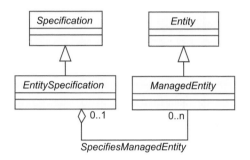

Figure 3.29 – Entity Specification/Entity Pattern

Figure 3.30 shows the use of the Entity Specification/Entity pattern in the Service domain.

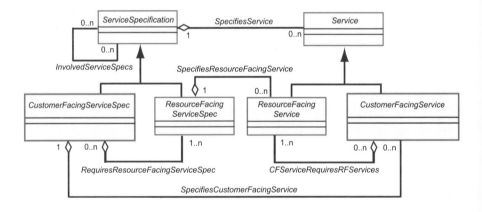

Figure 3.30 – Service Specification/Service Use of the Entity Spec/Entity Pattern

Typically, there will be an ABE for the specification and an ABE for the entity characterized by the specification within each SID domain or complex ABE. A complex ABE is one that decomposes into a number of other ABEs or into a number of nested ABEs. The reason for this is that each of these business concepts is complex enough to contain a number of related and dependent business entities. Figure 3.31 shows the Service Specification ABE to illustrate this point.

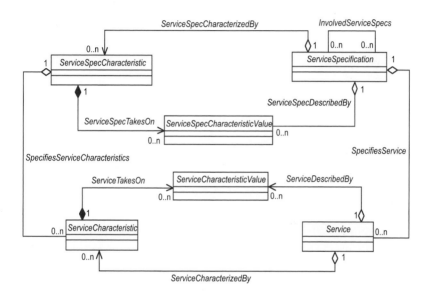

Figure 3.31 – Service Specification ABE

Using the SID Framework to Organize Current Information Models

The SID Framework's domains and ABEs can also be used to organize current information models. Employing the framework provides a consistent method in which to organize models. Using the framework also means that a common vocabulary is used to communicate the contents of the model. It also provides a common reference point that facilitates locating model contents.

Evaluating SID Conformance Using TM Forum NGOSS Compliance Criteria

The SID compliance testing strategy focuses on promoting interoperability by employing levels of SID compatibility. Levels of SID compatibility measure a solution's or a component's compatibility with SID domains, ABEs, business entities, and attributes. As the level of compatibility increases, the amount of forecasted integration work decreases. Please note that the scope of these levels of compatibility deals with the parts of the SID that are exposed via XSDs and the XML documents that are exchanged between and among components.

The true focus and context of SID compatibility is at the ABE level, since ABEs define the scope of a solution.

The SID levels of compatibility are:

• Level 1 compatibility: The content of the model is compatible with a subset of the SID ABEs that define its domain coverage. This provides two interacting components/solutions with a common vocabulary and model structure. The subset represents the scope of the component/solution, expressed in SID domains and ABEs.

• Level 2 compatibility: The component/solution has passed level 1 compatibility and the content of the ABE, part of the domain coverage and defined in the model, contains the ABE's core business entity or entities. A core business entity is an entity upon which other entities within the ABE are dependent. For example, Service in the Service ABE. A solution/component should strive to attain as high a level of SID compatibility as possible. A core entity is also an entity whose absence in the ABE would make the ABE incomplete.

• Level 3 compatibility: The component/solution has passed level 2 compatibility and the required attributes of the ABE's core entity or entities are defined in the model.

- Level 4 compatibility: The component/solution has passed level 3 compatibility and dependent entities within the ABE's are defined in the model. A dependent entity is one whose instances are dependent on an instance of a core entity. For example, a ServiceCharacteristic instance within the Service ABE is dependent upon an instance of the Service entity.

- Level 5 compatibility: The component/solution has passed level 4 compatibility and the required attributes of the ABEs dependent entities are defined in the model.

- Level 6 compatibility: The component/solution has passed level 5 compatibility and all attributes of the ABE's core entities are defined in the model.

- Level 7 compatibility: The component/solution has passed level 6 compatibility and all attributes of the ABE's dependent entities are defined in the model.

A solution/component should strive to attain the highest level of SID compatibility. Level 3 should be a minimum objective.

Evaluating Potential Application Acquisitions and (Potential) Partner Application(s) Using NGOSS SID Compliance Criteria

As more and more service providers adopt NGOSS's eTOM and SID frameworks, they are requiring that independent software vendors (ISV) and B2B partners comply/conform to NGOSS principles. From a SID perspective, the NGOSS compliance criteria can be used evaluate the conformance of an ISV's applications to the SID. The higher the level of conformance the easier it should be to integrate an ISV's application into an NGOSS-enabled environment. Compliance also extends to internal applications and those of (potential) partners.

A service provider should require that an independent software vendor's, internal, or a partner's application be at least at level 3 conformance.

Using the SID Framework to Organize Use Cases

As use cases represent functionality inherent in an application, the eTOM is often used to organize use cases. If this is the case, then the ABEs associated with Use Cases can be found by using the eTOM/SID mapping. This mapping relates level two eTOM processes with level 1 SID ABEs.

The SID provides an alternative organization framework for use cases and is often an attractive technique to use when employing object-oriented development. Using the SID in this way groups all use cases whose primary focus (managing the life cycle of an ABE) is the ABE under which the use cases are grouped. For example, the Applied Customer Billing Rates ABE organizes all rating use cases; the Product Offering Price Rules organizes all use cases that manage the life cycle of product offering pricing rules.

Implementing the Technology-Neutral Architecture (Interaction Architecture)

The importance of use cases and contracts was described in the previous chapter. These two Technology-Neutral Architecture artifacts should always be considered for an implementation of NGOSS. Additionally, the artifact, sequence diagrams, should be considered, as it can serve as a bridge between use cases and contracts.

A summary of implementing other aspects of the Technology-Neutral Architecture is also included in this section.

Implementing Use Cases and Contracts

Use cases serve as one of the first artifacts (after eTOM/SID mappings) that describe the interaction between a user and a system expressed in terms of the business entities involved in the interaction. So, there shouldn't be a question as to whether use cases, or some other form of artifact that describes the interaction between a user and a system, should be implemented. Since use cases are an integral part of NGOSS the discussion here will assume they are used to describe the interaction.

Within NGOSS, a distinction is made between business view and system view use cases. System view use cases represent further refinements of business view use cases. Refinements can include the decomposition of a business view use cases into more discrete use cases and/or adding more detail to the description of the use case. For example, extension points may not be added until the system view is defined. An extension point is another use case that may be invoked as part of the execution of a use case.

To some NGOSS implementers, the distinction between business view and system view use cases may not be important. There are many reasons for not maintaining the distinction:

• The benefit, or lack of, realized by maintaining two views

• The interest that an NGOSS implementer has in maintaining the distinction

• The effort an NGOSS implementer has to expend maintaining the link between a use case and use cases into which it decomposes

• The inability of current tools to consolidate the two views when necessary.

Sequence diagrams represent a first step in formalizing a use case's transformation into a contract. An NGOSS implementer must ask the question "Does constructing a sequence diagram for each use case make sense?" The answer to this often lies in the complexity of a use case. The benefits realized by developing a sequence diagram for simple use cases may not justify the cost to develop it.

As the basic unit of interoperability, contracts are integral to an NGOSS implementation. Contracts specify an interface definition, much like an API, and also provide a traceability mechanism that links the contract to other NGOSS artifacts, such as eTOM processes, SID entities, sequence diagrams, and so forth.

A contract's purpose is much the same as that of a traditional application development specification.

A business contract contains:

- A header part, which includes the name, identifier, version of the contract

- A descriptive part, which includes the goal, description, and search criteria

- A functional part, which includes associated business processes, pre- and post-conditions, and interaction points

- A non-functional part, which includes deployment, organizational, legal, and miscellaneous aspects of the contract

- A management part, which includes management activities, responsible management roles, and so forth

- A business model part, which includes references to use case diagrams, interaction diagrams, behavior diagrams, business artifacts, and so forth.

A business view contract may transform (at the implementer's discretion) into a system view contract. A system view contract contains the same parts as a business view contract along with additional details provided for certain parts. For example, the management part contains aspects of policies that deploy and monitor the contract.

The question left to the NGOSS implementer is whether or not to use NGOSS contracts to replace or augment existing interface/development specifications. The key here, from an NGOSS perspective, is there is a common way to define the services made available within a contract. And, when implementing contract definitions within your organization, many options exist. For example, someone defining a contract may choose to only define the header, descriptive, functional, and model parts of a contract. Within the functional part, someone may choose only to list the interaction points, since the business model part links the contract to use cases, which contain the pre- and post-conditions as well as to the eTOM business processes.

Implementing Other Aspects of the Technology-Neutral Architecture (TNA)

This section provides some guidance on implementing other aspects of the Technology-Neutral Architecture. Extensive experience with the implementation of most of these principles has yet to be achieved. Therefore, implementation guidance is limited.

These aspects include:

- Separation of business process from component implementation

- Presence of a security-enabled architecture

- Presence of a policy-enabled architecture

- A shared information and data environment (already presented as the SID)

- Distribution transparency.

The separation of business process from component implementation is a key TNA principle. Embedding business process logic within a component limits the components reusability and should be avoided. When enhancing applications, developers should consider removing business logic from existing components. Whether enhancing existing applications or developing new applications the use of an off-the-shelf or in-house developed process management application should be considered.

Security is also an important aspect of the architecture. Each NGOSS framework specification or recommendation should clearly state the method by which it achieves security by highlighting its behavior against each security context. Security context includes confidentiality, availability, integrity, and attribution (non-repudiation).

Current Operational Support Systems (OSS's) are typically built in an "one-off" fashion according to the needs of a specific enterprise. In contrast, an OSS that contains a policy-based management system will be built to a more generic set of requirements. The functionality of a policy-managed OSS will be constrained to the requirements of any given user through the application of policy.

The system builder determines the need for policy, based on the operational requirements of the system user. Current OSS's are typified by the following characteristics:

• Many owners share large distributed systems, and, thus, multiple management systems will be required to cooperatively manage the systems(s) as a functional whole

• The correlation of management activities requires one or more special correlation systems

• A single management system cannot handle the set of unique problems associated with each component within a distributed system

• User behavior may differ from one subsystem to another, making it difficult for one single management system to manage user behavior across systems and subsystems.

Systems that exhibit one or more of the above characteristics are prone to failure because, if the management system fails, there is no backup management mechanism. Policy-based management systems have been proposed to solve the preceding list of problems. This has two attendant benefits. First, it improves the reusability of the management systems. Second, it increases the availability of the overall system or subsystem.

So, some form of policy should be embodied within an NGOSS system (application). It may be implemented as purely policy-based (policy modeled) or via some type of user-defined rules engine.

The heart of distribution transparency is a registry, which provides a logical view of the all the information about deployed distributes systems. Information contained in the repository includes registration information for each business process, component, and contract deployed within the scope of the repository and the advertising information for each contract instance. In addition, the repository contains all security and policy information associated with each component, contract, and contract instance. The repository may be implemented as a single database, a group of co-operating peer databases, or a hierarchical group of interoperating databases.

Chapter Four

Implementing NGOSS - Vendor Case Study

This chapter presents an independent software vendor's NGOSS implementation experience. MetaSolv Software is a member of the NGOSS program development team. As an early adopter of NGOSS principles, MetaSolv has employed NGOSS artifacts as they became available for use. Through use of these artifacts, MetaSolv has realized many of the benefits associated with the NGOSS program, including reduction in development time, reduction in the time it takes to interface with other applications, and a common way in which to describe functionality (both process and information) embodied within its applications.

This particular case study only applies to one MetaSolv product, however other products implement NGOSS in similar fashions.

Implementing NGOSS

This section describes early use of the eTOM and proto-SID Aggregate Business Entities (called business objects here) before the TM Forum initiated the NGOSS program. This early use facilitated the transition to implementing the NGOSS program.

Pre-NGOSS Use of eTOM

Not being a service provider placed some limits on the use of the eTOM (formerly called the TOM when first used). Two uses were found for the eTOM:

• Demonstrating the applications support for eTOM business processes

• Providing a framework for organizing business objects.

Many independent software providers use the eTOM to show the business processes supported by their applications. The eTOM provides a standard way in which vendors demonstrated this coverage. Prior to NGOSS, the level of detail provided by the TOM was what is now referred to as level 2 eTOM processes. In Figure 4.1, the dark-shaded processes are those covered by the application. Other vendors used a similar method.

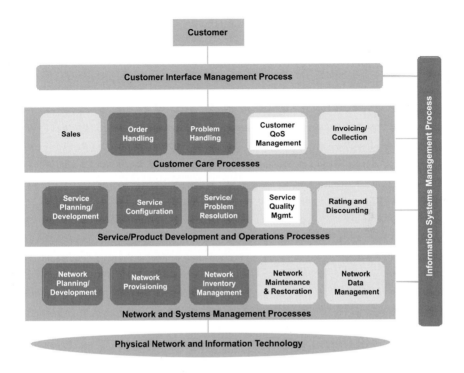

Figure 4.1 – TOM Process Coverage by an Application

There was also a desire to have a framework for organizing business objects. The term business object as used at MetaSolv was a forerunner of the SID's Aggregate Business Entity. It represented a cohesive group of entities, such as service requests and trouble tickets, whose life cycle was managed by a process.

Since the SID Framework was not yet in existence, the TOM was employed. The framework was based on the process groupings in Figure 4.1. Note that a number of the process groupings are now represented in the eTOM as level 2 processes.

Figure 4.2 shows how business objects were organized using the TOM as the framework. This framework represented an early version of the eTOM level 2 to SID ABE mappings that exist today.

```
Order Handling [2.2]
          Service Requests [2.2.1]
                    Service Requests. [2.2.1.1]
                    Service Request Service Items [2.2.1.2]
                    Service Items [2.2.1.3]
                    Product Service Requests (PSR) [2.2.1.4]
                    Access Service Requests [2.2.1.5]
                              Switched Access Service Requests [2.2.1.5.1]
                              Special Access Service Requests [2.2.1.5.2]
                              Ring Access Service Requests [2.2.1.5.3]
                              Confirmation Notices [2.2.1.5.4]
                    Internal Service Requests [2.2.1.6]
                    Universal Service Orders (receive only) [2.2.1.7]
                    Directory Service Requests [2.2.1.8]
                    Service Request Worksheets [2.2.1.9]
                    Local Service Requests [2.2.1.10]
                    NPAC Subscription Version [2.2.1.11]
                    Develop Service Request Hierarchy [2.2.1.12]
          Product Sales [2.2.2]
                    Product Warranties [2.2.2.1]
          Services [2.2.3]
                    Network Consulting [2.2.3.1]
                    Network Implementation [2.2.3.2]
                    Network Operations [2.2.3.3]
          Partnership Management [2.2.4]
     Problem Handling [2.3]
          Trouble Tickets. [2.3.1]
          Trouble Ticket Notifications [2.3.2]
          Trouble Ticket Escalations [2.3.3]
```

Figure 4.2 – Forerunner of SID Framework

In Figure 4.2, the Order Handling process is "mapped" to the business objects whose lifecycle it manages. The business objects are indented under the Order Handling process.

There was also a need to show further decompositions of the TOM process groupings as the decompositions represented functionality contained within MetaSolv's applications. The framework was extended to depict processes that managed the business objects' lifecycles as shown in Figure 4.3. The processes shown under each business object represent the equivalent of today's eTOM level 3 processes.

```
Order Handling [2.2]
     Service Requests [2.2.1]
          Service Requests. [2.2.1.1]
                    Receive Service Request [2.2.1.1.1]
                    Complete Service Request [2.2.1.1.2]
                              Receive SR External Provider Confirmation [2.2.1.1.2.1]
                    Cancel Service Request [2.2.1.1.3]
                    Supplement Service Request [2.2.1.1.4]
                    View Service Request [2.2.1.1.5]
          Service Request Service Items [2.2.1.2]
                    Add Service Item to Service Request [2.2.1.2.1]
                    Remove Service Item from Service Request [2.2.1.2.2]
          Service Items [2.2.1.3]
                    Identify Service Item [2.2.1.3.1]
                    Modify Properties of Service Item [2.2.1.3.2]
                    Place Service Item "In Service" [2.2.1.3.3]
                    Disconnect Service Item [2.2.1.3.4]
          Product Service Requests (PSR) [2.2.1.4]
                    Receive Product Service Request [2.2.1.4.1]
                              Establish Customer Account [2.2.1.4.1.1]
                              Add PSR Order Information [2.2.1.4.1.2]
                              Associate Sales Modules to PSR [2.2.1.4.1.3]
                              Add PSR Services [2.2.1.4.1.4]
                                        Query for Dedicated Plant [2.2.1.4.1.4.1]
                                        Reserve for Dedicated Plant [2.2.1.4.1.4.2]
                              Change PSR Services [2.2.1.4.1.5]
                              Disconnect PSR Services [2.2.1.4.1.6]
                              Suspend PSR Services [2.2.1.4.1.7]
                              Restore PSR Services [2.2.1.4.1.8]
                              Move PSR Services [2.2.1.4.1.9]
                              Validate and Finish PSR Order [2.2.1.4.1.10]
                              Generate PSR Order Tasks [2.2.1.4.1.11]
                              Add a Billing Telephone Number [2.2.1.4.1.12]
                    Complete Product Service Request [2.2.1.4.2]
```

Figure 4.3 – TOM Used as Framework for Business Objects

In Figure 4.3, the processes that manage the life cycle of a Service Request are shown indented under Service Request business object.

NGOSS Implementation

Having an existing framework for business objects, now called Aggregate Business Entities, and having used the TOM to demonstrate process coverage by the application made the transition to implementing NGOSS much easier, since the SID Framework and the eTOM are two of NGOSS' cornerstones.

MetaSolv has implemented all key aspects of the NGOSS program, including the:

• NGOSS Lifecycle

• eTOM

• SID

• Technology-Neutral Architecture.

The remaining sections in this chapter describe implementation details for each of these NGOSS components. Also described are future directions for NGOSS at MetaSolv.

Implementing the NGOSS Lifecycle

MetaSolv uses the Rational Unified Process (RUP) to develop its software. Figure 4.4 depicts the RUP's phases and disciplines. RUP is an iterative, use-case driven approach to application development, two of the key characteristics of the NGOSS Lifecycle

Phases

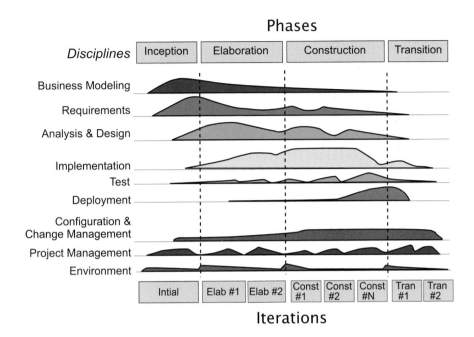

Disciplines	Inception	Elaboration	Construction	Transition

Business Modeling

Requirements

Analysis & Design

Implementation

Test

Deployment

Configuration &
Change Management

Project Management

Environment

Intial	Elab #1	Elab #2	Const #1	Const #2	Const #N	Tran #1	Tran #2

Iterations

Figure 4.4 – Rational Unified Process Phases and Disciplines

While RUP also embodies class models, it does not seem to represent a true model-driven approach to development, another key characteristic of the lifecycle. A model-driven approach based on the SID was added to the use of RUP at Metasolv.

The four NGOSS views are present within the various RUP disciplines. Business Modeling and Requirements represent the business view; Analysis and Design represent the system view; Implementation and Deployment represent the respective NGOSS implementation and deployment views.

MetaSolv does not maintain separate views. The business view is the starting point for development efforts. The process morphs the business view into the system view, which in turn is morphed into the implementation view, represented by APIs and user interfaces. A deployment view that represents the running application is kept as a separate view. The decision to keep what are, in effect, two views was based on a number of factors, including:

• The current absence of a model-driven approach to generating the implementation view(s)

• The lack of perceived benefit achieved by maintaining four separate views

• The cost to maintain four separate views

• The inability of tools used to maintain a link between the four NGOSS views.

Having the four NGOSS views present within RUP made providing the different NGOSS Lifecycle perspectives quite easy. The logical perspective is provided by use cases, business entities (using the SID as the base), and user interfaces. They are kept as a point-in-time view before the logical perspective morphs into the physical perspective. APIs and the deployed application provide the physical perspective. The development process likewise provides the Service Provider and Service Developer perspectives. As model-driven development continues to evolve, a separation between the consolidated business/system view and the implementation view may be introduced.

Use cases, an integral component of both NGOSS and RUP, are employed as a means to document application requirements. Formal NGOSS contracts are not employed. However, the spirit of NGOSS contracts is present via the use of Rational's Requisite Pro tool, which provides traceability, as defined by the NGOSS contract specifications, throughout the development life cycle. Traceability begins with specifying the link between use cases and application features and continues through to API specification and quality assurance testing to ensure that the deployed application satisfies documented features and requirements.

Implementing the eTOM

Not being a service provider meant that employing the eTOM in the typical fashion, as a process map, was not a possibility. However, the eTOM permeates MetaSolv's corporate environment, from Sales to Product Management to

Development. It was implemented in several different ways, including:

• As an early framework (pre-SID) for organizing business objects (already discussed)

• As a map that demonstrates application coverage of eTOM level 2 processes

• As a framework for organizing use cases

• As a tool to explain the data model in courses and workshops.

The eTOM has been used to demonstrate application coverage for about ten years. Early on, it became clear that prospects and customers wanted to see how applications supported eTOM processes. Having an industry standard process map makes it very easy to explain in well known terms what the application covers.

Figures 4.5 & 4.6 show how the eTOM is used for this.

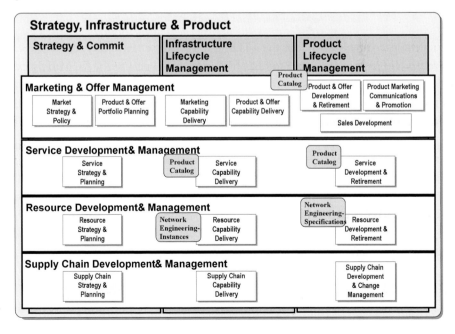

Figure 4.5 – Application Functionality Mapped to eTOM SIP Processes

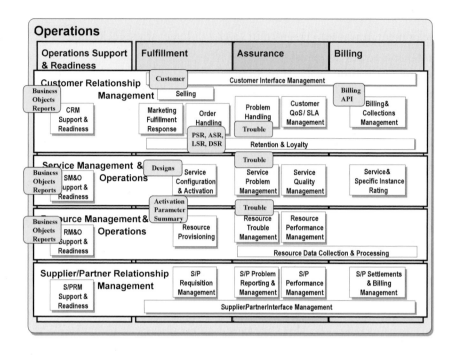

Figure 4.6 – Application Functionality Mapped to eTOM Operations Processes

Prior to the development of the eTOM, it was difficult to depict coverage of Strategy, Infrastructure, and Product (SIP) processes because the TOM only dealt with operational processes. With the advent of the eTOM and SIP processes this difficulty was removed as shown in Figure 4.5. The highlighted areas of this diagram represent Metasolv applications capabilities.

Support for operational processes is shown in Figure 4.6.

The RUP method of development has been in use for about four years at Metasolv. During the process of implementing RUP, a framework that would be used to organize use cases was a requirement. Rather than spend weeks and weeks attempting to define a proprietary framework, the eTOM was chosen.

The benefits realized by using the eTOM as a use case framework did not stop with the time saved in developing a framework. Using a common process framework along with its well-known terms means that use cases are easy to find and that their organization is easy to explain to everyone involved in the development process, including customers.

Figure 4.7 shows the eTOM framework used to organize use cases.

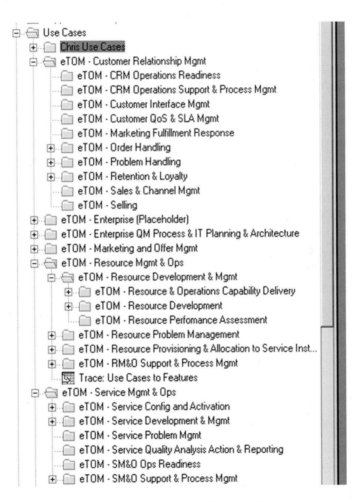

Figure 4.7 – Using the eTOM as a Use Case Organization Framework

The eTOM provides an effective, business-process-oriented way to introduce customer developers to the data model. For example, the Product & Offer Development & Retirement process supports the Product Catalog (SID Product Specifications and Product Offerings). Order Handling supports Service Requests and its various subclasses of customer and internal orders.

Implementing the SID

Implementing the SID Framework and the concept of Aggregate Business Entities (ABEs) was facilitated by the fact that a similar framework and a concept similar to ABEs were already in use. As mentioned in the Implementing the eTOM section of this chapter, the eTOM was used to organize groups of closely related business entities, called business objects. These groups of business objects, such as Customer, Party, and so forth, were easily correlated to the SID's ABEs and migrated to the SID Framework.

In addition to employing the SID Framework and ABE concept, the SID is used in a number of ways, including:

• Using the SID when developing new application extensions

• Using the SID to organize use case diagrams

• Using the SID as the foundation for an application integration framework.

Using the SID in New Development

Figure 4.8 shows the use of the SID within a new development project. The project employed the TM Forum guidelines for extending the SID model. The extensions are shown within the circled package in the figure. The class diagram in the figure shows how new entities were tied into existing SID entities (in this case ResourceSpecification) via an association.

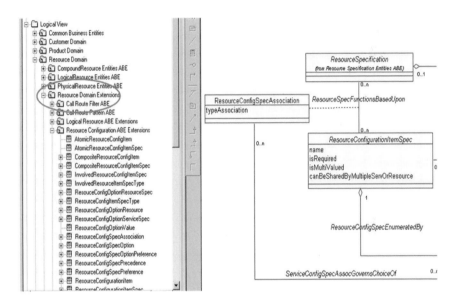

Figure 4.8 – SID Used in New Development Application

The SID was also used in another new development project as shown in Figure 4.9. On this project the guidelines for extending the SID were not followed in their entirety, which was a mistake. Because of this, it would be difficult to distinguish the SID core model from the extensions added to it (an oval shows one of the extensions). As a lesson learned, this was rectified during future projects.

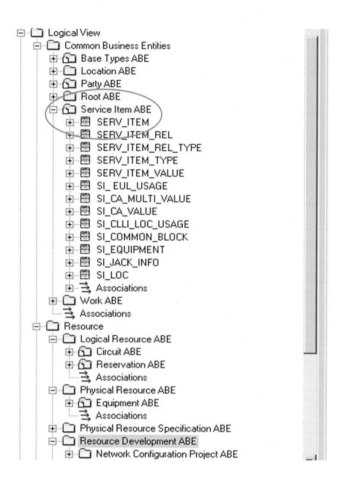

Figure 4.9 - Use of SID Where Extention Guidelines were not follwed

Currently, there is no attempt to maintain a single model based on the SID. The reason for this is that each project stands on its own and that the business view model of the SID and application specific extensions are used as a point-in-time model and not maintained once the project is completed. This decision was made based on the fact that current tools in use do not provide the ability to generate an implementation view model that suits MetaSolv's requirements and that the tools in use do not provide an easy way to keep the implementation view and other views synchronized.

As was mentioned, the four NGOSS views of the SID are not maintained. The business view morphs into the system view which morphs into the implementation view. A separate deployment view is maintained for each installation of the application.

Using the SID to Organize Use Cases

In the Implementing the eTOM section of this chapter, the use of the eTOM as a framework for organizing use cases was described. As an alternative, the SID Framework can also be used as an organizational framework for use cases. As an experiment, use case diagrams were organized using the SID Framework as shown in Figure 4.10. Organizing use cases in this manner represents a more object-oriented approach. No obvious benefits of one approach over the other were identified, particularly when there is now a mapping between SID ABEs and eTOM level 2 processes. This mapping makes it easy to find process-oriented artifacts or information-oriented artifacts that are organized using either framework.

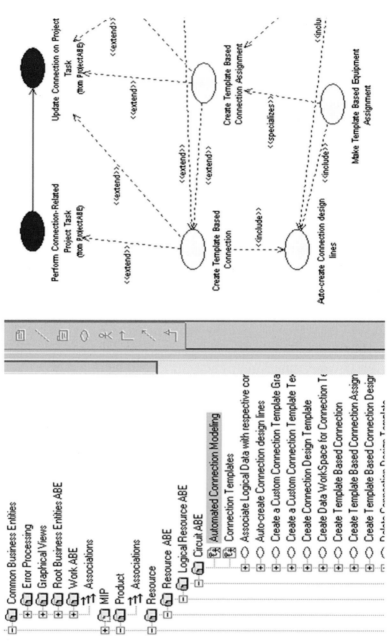

Figure 4.10 – Use Case Diagrams Organized Using the SID Framework

Using the SID as the Foundation for an Application Integration Framework

When the SID was first introduced, potential users thought that they would have to change their internal database structures in order to claim SID conformance. This perception was quickly dispelled as users found that one use of the SID was for it to become the foundation of application integration frameworks. This use of the SID exposes the internal data base structure in terms of the SID as XML schema with application-specific extensions as described in the Implementing the SID chapter of this book.

MetaSolv began using the SID in this way several years ago, before SID XML schema had been developed. The integration framework used the OSS/J Core Business Entity (CBE) schema, in existence at that time and based on the SID. The following two figures provide examples of the schema.

```
<complexType name="ServiceValue">
        <complexContent>
            <extension base="cbecore:EntityValue">
                <sequence>
                    <element name="mandatory" type="boolean" nillable="true"
minOccurs="0"/>
                    <element ref="cbeservice:startMode" minOccurs="0"/>
                    <element name="serviceKey" type="cbeservice:ServiceKey"
nillable="true" minOccurs="0"/>
                    <element ref="cbeservice:serviceState" minOccurs="0"/>
                    <element name="subscriberId" type="string" nillable="true"
minOccurs="0"/>
                </sequence>
            </extension>
        </complexContent>
    </complexType>
    <element name="baseStartMode" type="string"/>
    <element name="startMode" type="cbeservice:StartMode" substitutionGroup="cbeservice:
baseStartMode"/>
    <simpleType name="StartMode">
        <restriction base="string">
            <enumeration value="UNKNOWN"/>
            <enumeration value="AUTO_BY_ENV"/>
            <enumeration value="AUTO_BY_DEVICE"/>
            <enumeration value="MANUAL_BY_PROVIDER"/>
            <enumeration value="MANUAL_BY_CUSTOMER"/>
            <enumeration value="ANY"/>
        </restriction>
    </simpleType>
```

Figure 4.11 – CBE Service Domain XML Schema Fragment

Figure 4.11 shows a fragment of the CBE Service domain containing the SID-like Service entity. As with the SID schema, each domain, such as Product, Service, and Resource, is contained within its own schema. Note that this example of the Service entity employs all the SID attributes. If the application does not use all the SID attributes and/or associations, then another set of schema would be developed that represent a restriction base of the SID entities. Restriction base is explained in the Implementing SID as Part of an Application Integration Framework section in the previous chapter.

These schema are used to define another set of schema that contain application-specific extensions to the SID. The next figure shows an application-specific extension to the Service entity (using the Service entity as an extension base from Figure 4.12).

```
<complexType name="MetaSolvServiceValue">
        <complexContent>
                <extension base="cbeservice:ServiceValue">
                        <sequence>
                                <element name="serviceKey" type="metasolv-service:
MetaSolvServiceKey" minOccurs="0"/>
                                <element name="parentSpecKey" type="metasolv-service:MetaSol
vServiceSpecificationKey" minOccurs="0"/>
                                <element name="describingSpecificationKey" type="metasolv-
service:MetaSolvServiceSpecificationKey" nillable="true" minOccurs="0"/>
                                <element name="parentServiceKey" type="metasolv-service:
MetaSolvServiceKey" minOccurs="0"/>
                                <element name="externalServiceKey" type="string"
minOccurs="0">
```

Figure 4.12 – Application-Specific Extension XML Schema Fragment

The application-specific extensions are then used to construct domain schema containing information payloads for operations (similar to NGOSS contracts). An illustrative figure is not shown here, as the schema resemble those shown in the Implementing NGOSS chapter of this book.

Implementing the Technology-Neutral Architecture (Interaction Architecture)

The two key Technology-Neutral Architecture (TNA) artifacts, use cases and contracts, play a prominent role in the application development process. Another aspect of the TNA, separation of business process from component implementation also plays an important part in the application.

Technology-Neutral Contracts

The role use cases play has been described throughout this book. Therefore, no further discussion of them will be included here. But what place do NGOSS contracts play? Their use was described briefly earlier in this chapter.

To review, the major parts of a contract are:

• Header part

• Description part

• Functional part

• Non-Functional part

• Management part

• Business model part.

The implementation of the business view contract parts is described here, since the parts of a business view contract and a system view contract are the same. The detailed contents of each part are not described here; only examples are used to provide a glimpse of how contract parts and details are spread across MetaSolv's application development artifacts.

For simplicity, it is assumed that there is a one-to-one correspondence between a contract (equivalent to a Metasolv use case definition and API definition) and a use case, and that a use case equates to a level 3 eTOM process. Also, as shown earlier in this chapter, SID ABEs are used to organize use case diagrams. These associations bind a number of contract parts together by employing a use case as the central concept. APIs are then developed to support one or more use cases.

The Non-Functional and Management parts are not implemented, as these parts seemed more suited to a service provider.

Figure 4.13 shows the use case template employed in the application development process. It contains a number of details, such as the Header, Description, and Functional parts of a contract.

<The Project>   0/0/0000 0:00 AM
UC Spec: <Use Case Name>

Table of Contents

Figure 4.13 – Use Case Template

Figure 4.14 shows how use cases are traced back to features, or business capabilities, that are a detail of the Functional part of a contract. The requirement properties that support features for the use case are chosen from a list of features shown in the bottom pop-up in the figure.

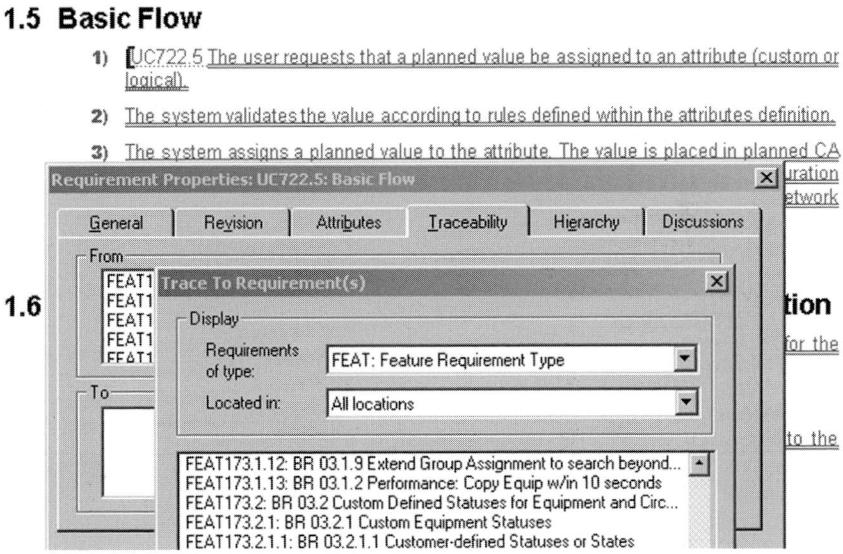

1.5 Basic Flow

1) [UC722.5 The user requests that a planned value be assigned to an attribute (custom or logical).

2) The system validates the value according to rules defined within the attributes definition.

3) The system assigns a planned value to the attribute. The value is placed in planned CA

Figure 4.14 – Tracing Use Cases to Requirements

Figure 4.15 shows the relationship between a development specification for an API and one or more use cases. Sequence and activity diagrams are used for more complex APIs. The use case realization section circled relates the API to the use cases implemented by it.

Table of Contents

Figure 4.15 – Application Development Specification Tie to Use Cases

In summary, while the development process does not employ a "pure" NGOSS contract and all of its parts, the combination of use cases, API development specifications, and tools provide the key parts of a contract.

Separation of Business Process from Component Implementation

While the application is not constructed of NGOSS specified components, it does maintain a separation of business process from other application functionality. This separation is implemented via the use of a work management feature of the application.

Figure 4.16 shows a work management user interface used to access other functionality in the application. In this figure selecting a DESIGN task invokes a connection design "component",as shown in Figure 4.17.

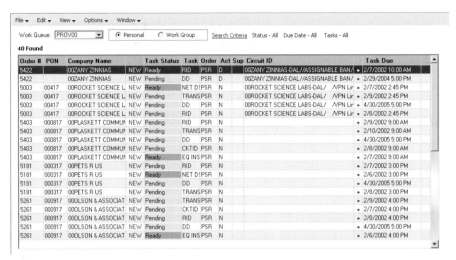

Figure 4.16 – Work Management Access to "Components'

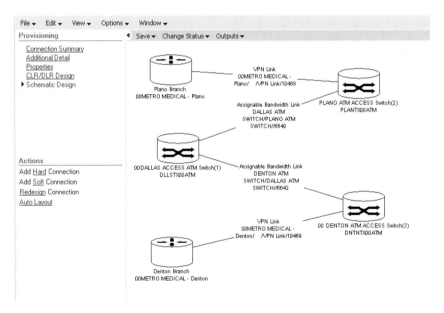

Figure 4.17 – Connection Design "Component" Accesses by Work Management

Not embedding business process logic within connection design means that other parts of the application can make use of the connection design logic. This type of implementation is true to the NGOSS separation of business process from component implementation.

Future Directions on Implementing NGOSS

The implementation of NGOSS does not and will not end with what this chapter describes. Research and development is underway to extend the use of a model-driven (and thus, more NGOSS-like) approach to development, where the SID system view drives the generation of object classes and operation signatures. This follows work in progress being undertaken by the OSS through Java™ Initiative. Note that extending the use of model-driven development may also necessitate splitting the combined business/system/implementation view into a logical (business/system) view and a physical (implementation) view.

Also in progress is the use of newly released SID XML schema to enhance the application integration framework. The generation of application-specific XML schema extensions to the SID is also being considered.

Chapter Five
Assessing an NGOSS Implementation

Assessment of an NGOSS implementation can include many facets. An enterprise may wish to assess the implementation of any or all of NGOSS' components such as the SID, the eTOM, and the Technology-Neutral Architecture. The scope may include one or more applications or business processes. This chapter describes the key aspects of an assessment.

Project Objectives and Scope

An NGOSS assessment is meant to answer one or more of the following questions:

- Are NGOSS artifacts being used to their fullest extent?

- Are NGOSS artifacts being used as recommended?

- Are there any new uses of NGOSS artifacts being employed?

A number of objectives may characterize an NGOSS assessment, depending on the state of an enterprise's NGOSS implementation. Objectives can include:

- Identifying a starting point for NGOSS implementation

- Mapping the current state of models and applications to NGOSS comparable artifacts, such as the eTOM

- Measuring the degree of conformance to and the use of NGOSS artifacts for an ongoing NGOSS implementation.

For example, an enterprise may have already implemented the SID and is interested in implementing the eTOM. In this case, one objective is to measure the degree of alignment to the SID, while another objective is to identify a starting point for eTOM implementation.

The first objective may not seem appropriate for a project labeled as an NGOSS assessment. However, this is an important first step in implementing NGOSS. Achieving this objective may be accomplished by assessing the readiness of an organization for taking on an NGOSS implementation. This objective may be achieved by including the second objective as part of the assessment. Also included may be the enterprise's willingness to accept change (This subject is the topic of a number of books on change management and is outside the scope of this book).

The second objective can be achieved by analyzing the gap between the current state and comparable NGOSS artifacts. The results of the gap analysis are used to identify short- and long-term implementation goals. NGOSS compliance/conformance criteria can assist in performing the analysis.

The third objective can also be achieved by applying NGOSS compliance/conformance criteria. Additionally, the assessment may include comparing potential uses of NGOSS artifacts to the uses of the artifacts being employed by an enterprise.

As described in the Implementing NGOSS chapter of this book, an enterprise does not have to implement an NGOSS artifact in total. For example, an enterprise may only be interested in the operational processes of the eTOM, or an enterprise may only be interested in the Customer and Product domains of the SID. The assessment must clearly state its scope in terms of the areas, such as domains, to be covered.

Assessment team

The assessment team may include:

- Project manager

- SID expert

- eTOM expert

- Technology-Neutral Architecture expert.

When assembling the team, the project manager is typically appointed first. The project manager identifies other team members, handles client relationships, manages and monitors the progress of the project, and serves as the facilitator during client engagements and during the delivery of the final report to the enterprise. The other roles on the team are optional. Their involvement depends on the NGOSS artifacts being assessed.

Assessment Methodology

The project tasks include an investigation phase, which include documentation review and interviews of key enterprise staff. Collation of material from this phase (documents, notes and so forth) then feed into the analysis phase, which is followed by recommendations. A formal document and/or a presentation communicates the recommendations to the client. The enterprise's review of this document may dictate that minor clarifications or corrections be made.

The time taken by each task depends on the scope of the project. Assessments should be time-boxed. The amount of time to perform all tasks and the duration of the assessment should be estimated prior to the start of the assessment.

The tasks are shown in Figure 5.1.

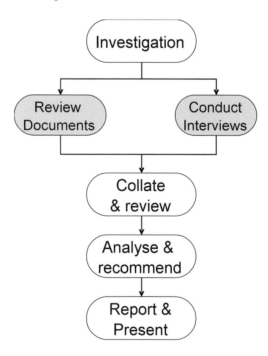

Figure 5.1 – NGOSS Assessment Methodology

During the investigation phase the assessment team gathers documents and conducts interviews with individuals familiar with the scope of the project. The documents provide a glimpse of the current state of an NGOSS implementation or the current state of the enterprise's applications and business processes within the scope of the project. Application documents may include database schema, information models, use cases, and so forth. Process documents may include process flow diagrams, use cases, mapping of current process to the eTOM, and so forth.

The assessment team reviews the documents prior to conducting interviews. During the document review, team members assemble lists of questions to be asked during the interviews. Interviews should provide additional details about the state of the work being assessed. They are conducted via conference calls, face-to-face meetings, or even via email exchanges. Interviews also help clarify the scope and objectives of the project.

With the results of the interviews in hand, the team is prepared to collate the information contained in the assembled documents with the review results. This task may identify the need for further interviews with the enterprise's individuals involved in the project. It is a necessary preparatory step that ensures a complete analysis can be accomplished.

The next task involves preparing an analysis of each NGOSS component within the scope of the project and developing recommendations for taking the components forward in the implementation. Individuals employed by the enterprise may be involved in the analysis. For example, it may be necessary to involve a data architect when mapping the SID model to current data base(s). This analysis may include such deliverables as tables that map SID entities to current data stores within an application, maps of current processes to eTOM processes, and gaps identified between the Technology-Neutral Architecture and the current architecture employed by the enterprise.

The analysis deliverables become the input for developing recommendations. Recommendations may include increasing the level of conformance with SID ABEs, employing use cases and contracts as part of the enterprise's application development process, and further use of the eTOM within the enterprise. Recommendations may be broken down into short and long-term objectives for beginning or continuing the NGOSS implementation.

The final task in the assessment involves preparing an assessment report and delivering the report to the enterprise. One of the assessment team members, typically the project manager, should be present in person when delivering the report. Other members may be present via conference call, webex, or some other form of real-time interaction.

NGOSS Lifecycle Methodology Assessment

This section describes NGOSS Lifecycle Methodology assessment objectives, how to conduct the assessment, and sample recommendations made for the further use of the NGOSS Lifecycle Methodology.

Lifecycle Methodology Assessment Objectives

The objectives typically focus on Lifecycle principles (repeated here from the chapter Implementing NGOSS), such as:

• There are different communities, such as service providers, independent software vendors, system integrators, equipment vendors, users, business analysts, developers, and so forth, interested in NGOSS; each community must be able to look at a NGOSS solution from their own viewpoint

• NGOSS artifacts are transformed or morphed as they move from one view to another; associations exist between the artifacts in each view

• Use cases are evident in each NGOSS view

• Contracts, which are comprised of one or more use cases, are the basic unit of interoperability; a contract is a container that collects and carries information throughout the lifecycle

• Traceability and visibility provide a means to verify that required business, system, and implementation processes, policies and functionalities are realized (forward traceability)

• Traceability and visibility throughout the lifecycle is necessary to ensure that running and available services meet the specified needs of the business (backward traceability)

• An information model (the SID) is shared throughout the lifecycle as a common underlying foundation for all models; it is essential to assure specified requirements, processes, policies, and constraints can interoperate and are traceable.

Based on the Lifecycle principles, the assessment may include the following objectives:

• Assessing the presence and use of the four NGOSS views

• Assessing the employment of use cases and contracts

• Assessing the traceability of artifacts, such as contracts, from one view to another

• Assessing the use of the SID model (covered in the section that deals with assessing the implementation of the SID)

• Assessing the use of the Lifecycle steps.

The presence and use of the four NGOSS views is key to successfully implementing NGOSS. While an enterprise does not have to maintain separate views, it should be obvious that the four views were used for developing NGOSS inspired applications.

Use cases and contracts are employed in each NGOSS view. While an enterprise may not have adopted use cases, some form of artifact that describes the interaction between a system and a user should be part of an enterprise's application development process. Similarly, an objective of the assessment is to investigate the use of contracts or contract-like artifacts.

Traceability as artifacts such as the SID and contracts morph from one view to another is also assessed. This is critical to assure that the deployed solution meets business requirements.

The assessment of the use of the SID model is contained in a later section of this chapter. Use of the SID represents the presence of a model-driven approach to development.

The Lifecycle Methodology steps provide a process that can be used if a structured approach to application development is not in place. The assessment evaluates if the presence of such an approach is in place.

Conducting the Lifecycle Methodology Assessment

A review of an enterprise's application development process will typically provide an assessment of the implementation of the NGOSS Lifecycle Methodology. The application development process should achieve the same objectives as the NGOSS Lifecycle, although the process may achieve the objectives using a different set of steps. For example, the Rational Unified Process employs a use case driven approach to development through a series of phases that somewhat resemble the NGOSS Lifecycle.

The first step in the assessment should, therefore, include a review of the application development process employed. The assessor should map the current process to the steps in the SANRR methodology to ensure coverage by the current process. Any gaps should be reported with recommended adjustments. For example, if there is not an adequate scoping process defined in terms of NGOSS artifacts, such as the eTOM and SID, then their use should be recommended.

The current application development process should employ use cases, or a similar step in which requirements are gathered via a description of the interaction a user has with the system. Absence of a use case or use case like approach should be noted in the assessment. The process is then evaluated to see if use cases are employed in the definition of contracts. The lack of contracts or similar artifacts should also be noted.

The four NGOSS views are also critical to the successful development of an application. The current development process is assessed for the presence of the views, either maintained as four separate views or in some combinations of the views. If the process does not employ the views, then sufficient justification should be provided to explain why the views are not present and/or were not used.

Finally, the assessor investigates the ability to trace requirements from the business view through to the deployment view.

Lifecycle Methodology Recommendations

Recommendations are typically organized by Lifecycle Methodology objective, including:

• Recommendations regarding the presence and use of the four NGOSS views

• Recommendations regarding the employment of use cases and contracts (covered in the section on assessing the implementation of the Technology-Neutral Architecture)

• Recommendations regarding the traceability of artifacts, such as contracts, from one view to another

• Recommendations regarding the use of the SID model (covered in the section that deals with assessing the implementation of the SID)

• Recommendations regarding the use of the Lifecycle steps.

If evidence of presence of the four NGOSS views, business, system, implementation and deployment, is lacking, a recommendation is made to include them in the enterprise's application development process. The four views do not have to be individually present, but typically a logical and physical view should be present and recommended as a minimum.

Traceability from requirements to deployed solution has been emphasized throughout this book. A lack of traceability can be corrected by employing tools, such as Rational Rose Requisite Pro, that provide this level of traceability. Manual tracing is not recommended.

Lastly, if a development methodology, such as RUP or MDA, which employs steps similar to the Lifecycle steps is not in use, then the adoption of such a methodology would be recommended.

eTOM Assessment

This section describes eTOM assessment objectives, how to conduct the assessment, and sample recommendations made for the further use of the eTOM.

eTOM Assessment Objectives

The purpose of an eTOM assessment is to investigate the level of process maturity within an organization and whether the process architecture of the organization is aligned to, or can be easily mapped to the eTOM.

The three levels of maturity within an organization are recapped here:

Process Immature

Immature organizations have a very loose set of processes that are used to control and drive their mission critical operations. These processes vary widely across different business units, using different approaches and different terminology to describe the same things. Mission critical processes often depend on 'heroes' who understand the 'way things get done' to ensure the smooth operation of the organization. There is generally no end-to-end process owner for any of the key processes and there are typically loose hand-off points between the various process stages as the process responsibility moves from one business unit to the next.

Process Aware

Process Aware organizations have an awareness of the need to manage processes end to end. Processes are typically well documented in a standard template, although use of terminology varies from process to process. There may be an organization wide process framework but much of the organization may be unaware of the existence of this framework.

Process Centric

A process centric organization will have a well-defined set of operational processes for all mission critical business areas, each mapped to an organization wide process framework. Processes will be documented to a common template, using a common dictionary.

Conducting the eTOM Assessment

An eTOM assessment has three core aspects:

• An interview period is used to understand the attitude within the organization to process definition and adoption

• A detailed walk-through of critical processes is required to understand the level of detail being defined in the processes. This will also involve a mapping of the processes to the eTOM level 2 and level 3 processes

• A review of process development methodology and change control is also required to gain an understanding of the process maturity of the organization.

In all three cases it is essential that expert process architects are made available to participate fully in the assessment from as broad a representation across the organization as possible.

Interview

The purpose of the interview is to understand the broad attitude of the organization to the development and maintenance of processes. This interview is not a single interview but should be conducted in several stages:

- Executive interview

- Process architects/analyst interview

- Implementation engineers interview.

The executive interview is aimed at discovering the executive attitude to processes and their knowledge of how processes are defined and maintained. The executive attitude to ownership and accountability of processes is also important to understand. The level of executive commitment to process improvement has a strong bearing on the level of process maturity of the organization.

The process architect/analyst interview is aimed at gaining a detailed explanation of how processes are developed and maintained. It also focuses on the challenges the architect faces in gaining adoption of defined processes within the organization.

The implementation engineer interview is aimed at understanding the role processes play in the development lifecycle. In many cases a process immature organization will view the role of processes as something that is defined once the system has been built. In process mature organizations implementation engineers will recognize that systems are developed to implement processes.

Process Walkthrough

This is the body of the eTOM assessment and involves working with the process architects or process analysts to understand the organizations processes in general, how they are defined and how they are rolled out.

The mapping of the processes is described in detail in the Implementing eTOM section in the Implementing NGOSS chapter of this book.

Process Development Methodology

It is important for the assessment to pay as much attention to the internal processes for defining and changing processes, as it is to focus on the mapping of the process architecture to the eTOM. A mature process development methodology, supported by tools as necessary, is a critical part of an organizations overall process maturity.

At times too much focus can be placed on process flow modeling tools. It must be remembered that tools will not magically enable an organization to become process mature. They simply help an organization efficiently enact its inherent process maturity.

During this phase of the assessment attention should be paid not only to the process modeling approaches but also to the requirements capture methodology and the linkages to the overall solution development methodology.

eTOM Assessment Recommendations

The recommendations from an eTOM assessment should be divided into three general categories:

• Process structure recommendations

• Process definition tools, standards and methodology recommendations

• Organizational and executive recommendations.

Having done a mapping of the company's processes to the eTOM, process structure recommendations are aimed at the level of definition of processes. Companies will often find that they have several high level processes that cover a very wide range of responsibility. Breaking these high level processes down into a number of smaller processes makes them easier to manage and easier to assign ownership.

The methodology that the organization adopts for defining and updating processes is a critical part of the recommendations. Recommendations on consistency of terminology and consistency of structure are all important if the organization is to adopt a 'single' approach to process definition. There are many tools and standards available that help in the area of process flow definition and suitable recommendations surrounding the use of these tools and standards should comprise part of the final recommendations.

Finally the report should focus on the executive level actions that need to be taken to embed or improve the process maturity of the organization. Recommendations surrounding the appointing of board level owners for mission critical processes, the creation of a corporate process group, or the identification of process performance benchmarks and their incorporation into the organization balanced scorecard are all areas of possible recommendation depending on the maturity of the organization.

SID Assessment

This section describes SID assessment objectives, how to conduct the assessment, and sample recommendations made for the further use of the SID.

SID Assessment Objectives

SID assessment objectives can include recommendations regarding how the SID can be used, a measurement of the level of conformance to SID ABEs, and analysis of the current use of the SID. The objectives typically focus on the uses of the SID (repeated here from the chapter Implementing NGOSS), such as:

• Employing the SID as part of an application integration framework (SID UML model and XML schema)

• Focusing new/enhanced application development on the SID Framework, model, and addenda

• Using the SID Framework to organize current information models

• Evaluating conformance to the SID using TM Forum compliance program criteria

• Evaluating potential application acquisitions and (potential) partner applications using SID TM Forum compliance program criteria

• Using the SID Framework to organize use cases

Based on the uses of the SID, the assessment may include the following objectives:

• Assessment of the use of the SID for application integration

• Assessment of the use of the SID for new/enhanced development

• Assessment of the use of the SID for organizing current information models

• Assessment of conformance to the SID based on analyzing current UML models or database schema

• Assessment of the use of SID conformance criteria for evaluating acquisitions or partner applications

• Assessment of the use of the SID for organizing use cases.

Conducting the SID Assessment

Assessment of the Use of the SID for Application Integration

Assessment of the use of the SID for application integration involves investigating the use of SID or SID-like XML schema. A sample fragment of a SID schema representing the UrbanPropertyAddress, its attributes and its associations, is shown in Figure 5.2.

```
com.sid.CommonBusinessEntities.LocationABE.Entities.GeographicPlace.GeographicAddress.
UrbanProperty.Address
        <xs:complexType name="UrbanPropertyAddress" abstract="true">
            <xs:complexContent>
                <xs:extension base="SIDBusCm:GeographicAddress">
                    <xs:sequence>
                        <xs:element name="streetNrFirst" minOccurs="0"/>
                        <xs:element name="streetNrFirstSuffix" minOccurs="0"/>
                        <xs:element name="streetNrLast" minOccurs="0"/>
                        <xs:element name="streetNrLastSuffix" minOccurs="0"/>
                        <xs:element name="streetName" minOccurs="0"/>
                        <xs:element name="streetType" minOccurs="0"/>
                        <xs:element name="streetSuffix" minOccurs="0"/>
                        <xs:element name="locality" minOccurs="0"/>
                        <xs:element name="postcode" minOccurs="0"/>
                        <xs:element name="PropertyAddressAssociationForUrbanProperty
Address" minOccurs="0"/>
                    </xs:sequence>
                </xs:extension>
            </xs:complexContent>
        </xs:complexType>
```

Figure 5.2 – Sample Fragment of SID XML Schema

From an assessment perspective, independently created SID-like schema should follow the above structure and content. For example, there should be a separate schema for each SID domain. If using the SID schema directly no changes should be made to the schema, nor should enterprise-specific extensions be added directly to the SID schema. By doing this, updates to the SID schema would be difficult to adopt because enterprise-specific extensions would have to be re-introduced into the SID schema.

Assessment of the Use of the SID for New/Enhanced Development

Assessment of the use of the SID in new/enhancement development projects proceeds in a similar fashion to the assessment of the use of SID XML schema. A sample fragment extension made to the SID UML model is shown in Figure 5.3.

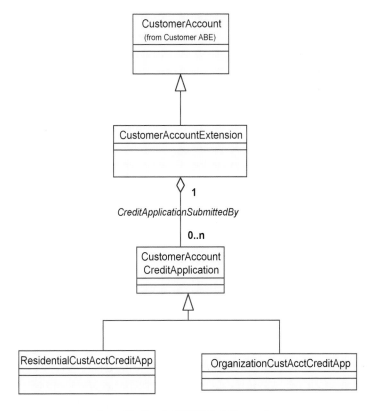

Figure 5.3 – Sample SID UML Model Fragment

Figure 5.3 shows a new business entity, CustomerAccountExtension, which holds attributes about a CustomerAccount not found in the base SID model. The CustomerAccountCreditApplication and its subclasses are added to the model and related to the extension entity. If there are no additional attributes needed for CustomerAccount, then the CustomerAccountCreditApplication entity can be directly related to the existing CustomerAccount SID entity.

Changes should not be made directly to SID entities, nor should enterprise-specific extensions be added directly to the SID entities. By making direct changes, updates to the SID model would be difficult to adopt because enterprise-specific extensions would have to be re-introduced into the model.

Key to a successful assessment is following the guidelines set forth in the Using the SID addendum when extending the SID. The addendum provides guidelines for adding attributes, adding entities, and adding associations, as well as recommended patterns to use when adding entities. It also contains naming guidelines for adding new ABEs, new entities, attributes and associations. The extent to which these guidelines are followed will influence the results of an assessment of this use of the SID.

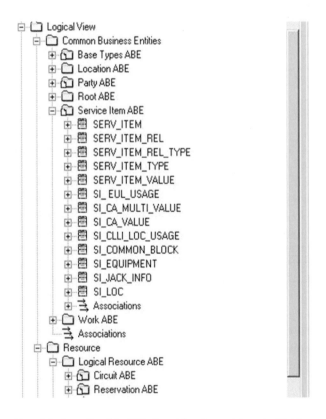

Figure 5.4 – Proper Use of the SID for Organizing a Current Information Model

Assessment of the SID for Organizing Current Models and Use Cases

This assessment determines if the SID Framework is being used to organize current information models and/or use cases. If neither use is employed, then the enterprise should consider employing one or both. If either is being employed, then the SID framework should not be compromised

A figure from the Implementing NGOSS Case Study chapter is included here to demonstrate the proper use of the SID Framework to organize a current information model.

In Figure 5.4, a new ABE is introduced to hold the entities that make up a Service Item rather than adding the entities to an existing SID ABE.

Assessment of Conformance to the SID

This form of assessment is suited for enterprises that are preparing to implement the SID or those implementing the SID. The assessment employs the SID conformance criteria to measure how closely a current model or schema matches the SID. The assessment can be conducted on an ABE by ABE basis.

The NGOSS Compliance team is, as of the writing of this book, investigating the use of automation to support this type of assessment. In the mean time, the assessment is conducted manually, using a mapping table as shown in Figure 5.5. Filled-out examples of these tables can be found in the next chapter.

	<<Entity Grouping Name>> Mapping	
<<Entity Name>> Attribute	SID Entity/Attribute <<SID Entity Name>>	Comment

Figure 5.5 – SID Mapping Template

The NGOSS SID assessor completes the table by collaborating with enterprise information architects or data base analysts. Entity groupings in the table can be based on SID ABEs or cohesive sets of current model entities or tables. For example, an entity grouping may represent the Product Offering ABE or a name by which this group of entities is known within the enterprise, such as Commercial Offering. The entity name is the name of current table or entity within the enterprise's schema or model. The SID entity name is the comparable entity from the SID model. Comments further clarify the mapping.

Upon completion of the mapping the assessor employs the SID conformance criteria to determine the degree of compatibility to a SID ABE. The criteria, previously provided in the Implementing NGOSS chapter are repeated here for the convenience of the reader.

The SID levels of compatibility are:

• Level 1 compatibility: The content of the model is compatible with a subset of the SID ABEs that define its domain coverage. This provides two interacting components/solutions with a common vocabulary and model structure. The subset represents the scope of the component/solution, expressed in SID domains and ABEs.

• Level 2 compatibility: The component/solution has passed level 1 compatibility and the content of the ABE, part of the domain coverage and defined in the model, contains the ABE's core business entity or entities. A core business entity is an entity upon which other entities within the ABE are dependent. For example, Service in the Service ABE. A solution/component should strive to attain as high a level of SID compatibility as possible. A core entity is also an entity whose absence in the ABE would make the ABE incomplete.

• Level 3 compatibility: The component/solution has passed level 2 compatibility and the required attributes of the ABE's core entity or entities are defined in the model(s).

- Level 4 compatibility: The component/solution has passed level 3 compatibility and dependent entities within the ABE's are defined in the model. A dependent entity is one whose instances are dependent on the existence of an instance of a core entity. For example, a ServiceCharacteristic instance within the Service ABE is dependent upon an instance of the Service entity.

- Level 5 compatibility: The component/solution has passed level 4 compatibility and the required attributes of the ABEs dependent entities are defined in the model.

- Level 6 compatibility: The component/solution has passed level 5 compatibility and all attributes of the ABE's core entities are defined in the model.

- Level 7 compatibility: The component/solution has passed level 6 compatibility and all attributes of the ABE's dependent entities are defined in the model.

The degree of compatibility is summarized by entity grouping in a bulleted list or a table. The higher the level, the more compatible the current model or schema is with the SID. An example of a compatibility table is shown in Figure 5.6.

	SID Compatibility	
<<Entity Grouping Name>>	<<SID ABE Name>>	Degree of Compatibility

Figure 5.6 – SID Compatibility Results

Assessment of the Use of the SID for Evaluating Other Applications

The mapping table and compatibility table can also be used to evaluate potential partner applications and to evaluate potential acquisitions from software vendors. If tables are available from the partner or the software vendor, then the tables should be requested. Otherwise, the potential partner or vendor should be willing to collaborate with the enterprise to produce the tables.

SID Assessment Recommendations

SID assessment recommendations typically are embodied in a roadmap for implementing the SID or evolving current use of the SID. Recommendations are based on the results of assessment objectives, are organized by uses of the SID, and categorized as short- and long-term objectives.

The two primary uses of the SID, as an integral part of an application integration framework and as a starting point for new/enhanced application development projects typically have a prominent position in the recommendations.

For example, suppose a service provider is considering entering into a partnership with another provider. The use of the SID as part of an application integration framework is key to the success of the partnership, as applications will have to interoperate. If the provider already uses the SID for internal applications integration, then the recommendations would focus on the proper use of the SID for this purpose. If not, then the recommendation would be to begin using the SID for this. The degree of compatibility with the SID also influences the success of the partnership. The higher the degree of compatibility, the easier it will be to map current data structures to SID ABEs and entities within the application integration framework. Recommendations may also include samples of possible application-specific extensions to the SID XML schema.

For new/enhanced development, recommendations may include employing the SID if it is not currently employed, renaming internal data structures if they are being redesigned, and using SID terminology in user interfaces and documentation. Recommendations are specific and not general. For example, a recommendation may be to change the name of Commercial Offering in user interfaces to Product Offering. SID compatibility should also play a part in measuring the success of SID implementation.

The other uses of the SID, while still important, are typically classified as long-term objectives.

Technology-Neutral Architecture (TNA) Assessment

This section describes TNA assessment objectives, how to conduct the assessment, and sample recommendations made for the further use of the TNA.

Technology-Neutral Architecture Assessment Objectives

TNA assessment objectives can include recommendations regarding how the TNA can be used and analysis of the current use of the TNA. The assessment typically focuses on the objectives/principles of the TNA, such as:

- Use of contract-defined interfaces

- Use of a technology-neutral component model

- Separation of business process from component implementation

- Presence of a security-enabled architecture

- Presence of a policy-enabled architecture

- A shared information and data environment (already presented as the SID)

- Distribution transparency.

Conducting the Technology-Neutral Assessment

The Technology-Neutral Architecture assessment typically proceeds from one objective to the next. The objectives can be placed in two groups for assessment purposes. The first group deals with contracts, components, and their implementation. The second group deals with the architecture that manages the implemented components. The second group includes assessment of the security-enabled architecture, the policy-enabled architecture, and distribution transparency.

The results of the NGOSS Lifecycle Methodology assessment may be a valuable input to the TNA assessment, as it also stresses the use of contracts and components. Therefore, the same techniques employed for the Lifecycle assessment regarding contracts and components can be used for this part of the TNA assessment. They are not covered here for that reason. However, contracts and components should be organized using the eTOM or SID frameworks. The assessor should determine if one of these standard frameworks is employed to do this.

Separation of business process from component implementation is covered here, as it is not part of the Lifecycle assessment. To enable reuse, business logic should not be embedded within a component's logic. The assessor should analyze components or component-like artifacts to determine if this NGOSS principle is being followed.

An assessment of the second group of principles follows the first. The assessor determines if there is an overarching security model in place. Use of the optional NGOSS policy architecture is then evaluated. Some type of similar architecture should be in place. Lastly, a framework that enables distribution transparency is evaluated. An important note here is that there is not a large body of practical implementations of this second group. As the NGOSS evolves and implementations include these aspects of the Technology-Neutral Architecture, additional assessment criteria will be put in place.

Technology-Neutral Assessment Recommendations

As with other assessment recommendations, the TNA assessment recommendations are organized by the objective of the individual assessment item. The recommendations report on how well the TNA principles were applied in the NGOSS implementation or how the current state of an enterprise's applications compare to the principles. Recommendations are organized within the same groupings used to conduct the assessment.

Recommendations regarding the first group may include:

• Organizing contracts and components using the eTOM or SID framework

• Removing business process logic from a component's logic

• Employing contract and component principles.

The recommendations may not imply an all-or-nothing approach to embracing these principles. For example, a step-wise approach may be recommended for the specification and development of contracts. This approach may begin with the contracts that manage the lifecycle of the entities contained within some number of SID ABE(s) or some number of processes that comprise a level 2 eTOM process.

Recommendations regarding the second group may include the implementation of a policy-enabled architecture application by application. Migrating to a security-enabled architecture, likewise, may be a step-wise process.

NGOSS *Distilled*

Chapter Six

NGOSS Assessment Example

This chapter provides a template of how an assessment report, based on the approach outlined in the previous chapter, should be structured. This report structure is suitable for an assessment of any Service Provider that is providing services ranging from traditional telecommunications services and mobile services to triple play DSL and cable providers. The focus of this assessment structure is to do a rapid analysis of the Service Provider's existing environment relative to NGOSS and to identify a roadmap to aligning with NGOSS. Future more detailed assessments may well be required in the future on specific aspects of alignment to NGOSS, but they are not addressed in this example.

Report Outline

A suggested outline and structure of an assessment report would be as follows

The remainder of this chapter outlines some examples and templates of what this report should contain and the appropriate level of content.

Section 1 - Project Overview & Executive Summary

The project overview and executive summary section of the assessment should describe the assessment objectives, the assessment methodology, the assessment team, the structure of the assessment report, and acknowledges those individuals within the enterprise who assisted the assessment team.

The assessment objectives would typically address the level of alignment of the Service Providers system or systems to the NGOSS standards and policies. The scope should be bounded to a speedy review and assessment of the system(s) from the following NGOSS perspectives:

- Alignment to the NGOSS SID

- Alignment to the NGOSS eTOM

- Alignment to the NGOSS Technology-Neutral Architecture principles

- Alignment of the implementation methodology to the NGOSS Lifecycle Methodology.

The Executive Summary should specifically provide a high level readout of the conclusions from the assessment. This is the only section of the report that is likely to be read by the senior executive team and as such it is essential in this section to clearly highlight the major gaps in NGOSS alignment and the key actions that must be carried out to address the biggest alignment gaps.

Section 2 - Assessment of Process Architecture

This section of the report is aimed at presenting the results of the assessment of the overall process architecture and how it aligns with the NGOSS eTOM including:

• Establish the scope of process work underway and planned

• Determine the extent of existing and possible future linkage with the TM Forum Enhanced Telecom Operations Map® (eTOM) Business Process Framework, and beyond this with other such external work

• Identify potential future opportunities and strategies for applying the TM Forum work, where helpful, within the IT area and more widely within the organization.

This section of the report should follow the outline of the three focus areas identified above, and provide results for each of these.

Section 2.1 - Scope of Process Work

It is important in this section to highlight the conclusions regarding the company's overall approach to process standardization. First among these conclusions should be the assessment of the level of process maturity across the organization. The three levels of process maturity are defined as process immature, process aware and process-centric. The remainder of this section of the report must be viewed in the context of the level of process maturity and so it is important that this is clearly stated up front, along with the rationale for this determination of process maturity. Items that might be included as part of this rationale include:

• Are the processes defined in a system-centric fashion or do they address the broad context across the organization and have an "end-to-end" business flows perspective?

• Does the organization have a single high level consistent view of processes across the whole organization or are all processes defined in isolation? If this exists it is likely to include a process framework.

Section 2.2 - Linkage of Process Architecture with eTOM

General
In this section the report should make general observations about the levels of process definition and their general relationship to the eTOM. Typically observations might include:

• Are the levels at which processes have been defined broadly equivalent in granularity with the eTOM levels. If so this eases comparison and makes the prospects for relating the processes themselves more straightforward. It should be noted that eTOM provides an enterprise-wide model down to level 3 for the area covered by these business-oriented processes.

• Has the organization adopted similar philosophies to the eTOM, such as the separation between Customer, Service and Resource/Network layers.

• How does the approach for decomposing processes relate to the approach adopted by the eTOM.

Analysis of Specific Processes

In this section the individual processes across the organization are cataloged and then mapped to the eTOM processes. This is likely to include processes covering the complete scope of the eTOM Operations process area (and to a lesser extent the Strategy, Infrastructureand Product (SIP) and Enterprise Management (EM) process areas). However, a consistent approach is needed to represent the analysis and mapping of these processes. Two examples of how this should be represented in a report are shown below:

Analysis of Processes

"Create" Processes

The "Create" processes cover the introduction of new customers and related activities. Two level 3 processes are defined: Create New Customer and Manage Install Activity.

Create New Customer

Create New Install maps to eTOM 1.F.1.5.3: Receive PO and Issue Orders
Note: Workforce orders are equivalent to hand-off to RM&O/OS&R in eTOM
Amend Install Order maps to eTOM 1.F.1.5.4: Track Order & Manage Jeopardy
Note: there is less emphasis on jeopardy handling than in the eTOM process

Manage Install Activity

Complete Install Order maps to eTOM 1.F.1.5.5: Complete Order

No significant conflicts with eTOM observed.

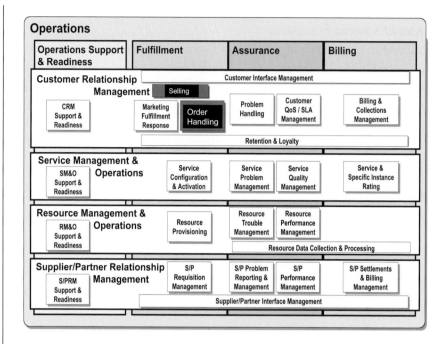

Operations

Operations Support & Readiness	Fulfillment	Assurance	Billing

Customer Relationship Management

Customer Interface Management

Selling

| CRM Support & Readiness | Marketing Fulfillment Response | Order Handling | Problem Handling | Customer QoS / SLA Management | Billing & Collections Management |

Retention & Loyalty

Service Management & Operations

| SM&O Support & Readiness | Service Configuration & Activation | Service Problem Management | Service Quality Management | Service & Specific Instance Rating |

Resource Management & Operations

| RM&O Support & Readiness | Resource Provisioning | Resource Trouble Management | Resource Performance Management |

Resource Data Collection & Processing

Supplier/Partner Relationship Management

| S/PRM Support & Readiness | S/P Requisition Management | S/P Problem Reporting & Management | S/P Performance Management | S/P Settlements & Billing Management |

Supplier/Partner Interface Management

"Create" Processes – Footprint on eTOM OPS Processes

The equipment-oriented process steps (for example, Load Install) are in line with eTOM interaction with SM&O and RM&O processes, but the detail is hidden as the business-oriented processes treat these as "automatic" activities handled below the level of visibility of the user. As part of this, interaction with Manage Workforce (within RM&O Support & Readiness) would handle workforce orders, scheduling and so forth. Modifications for billing/ payment etc would be handled in eTOM by interaction with Billing & Collections Management.

These business-oriented processes can be mapped to a "footprint" on eTOM as shown in the figure below. Most of the process activity is within Order Handling in eTOM terms, but the Selling process is also involved.

"Billing" Processes

The "Billing" processes cover customer billing and related activities. Three level 3 processes are defined: Manage Billing, Manage Payments and Manage Collections. Some differences in terminology with eTOM were observed and are commented upon below.

Manage Billing

Manage Paper Billing maps to eTOM 1.B.1.8.3: Create & Deliver Bill
Suppress Bill maps to eTOM 1.B.1.8.3: Create & Deliver Bill
Note: current eTOM definition may need enhancement
Manage Billing Control maps to eTOM 1.B.1.8.4: Manage Customer Billing

Note: current eTOM definition may need enhancement

Manage Payments

Collect Due Payment maps to eTOM 1.B.1.8.5: Manage Collection
Manage Payment Method maps to eTOM 1.B.1.8.4: Manage Customer Billing
Manage Adjustments maps to eTOM 1.B.1.8.2: Apply Pricing, Discounting & Rating

Manage Collections

Collect Outstanding Payments maps to eTOM 1.B.1.8.1: Manage Customer Billing Inquiries
Note: terminology differences (for example "collections" used for normal payment handling in eTOM)
Manage Customer Risk maps to eTOM 1.B.1.8.1: Manage Customer Billing Inquiries
Note: current eTOM definition may need enhancement

Manage Debt maps to eTOM 1.B.1.8.1: Manage Customer Billing Inquiries

Note: current eTOM definition may need enhancement

Manage Credit Check maps to eTOM 1.F.1.5.2: Authorize Credit

Note: this is positioned as part of Order Handling in eTOM – this does not represent a mismatch since process grouping is a natural part of mapping eTOM to an organization, but may suggest review is appropriate to confirm current positioning is valid

No significant conflicts with eTOM were observed.

This area has been more deeply analyzed in the business-oriented processes than in the current level of detail published for eTOM, possibly reflecting the importance for the business in managing customer relationships over billing-related issues.

There is consequently an opportunity to lead industry thinking in this area by participation in the ongoing eTOM development on this topic in particular.

These business-oriented processes can be mapped to a "footprint" on eTOM as shown in the figure below. The process activity is centered on Billing & Collections Management within eTOM.

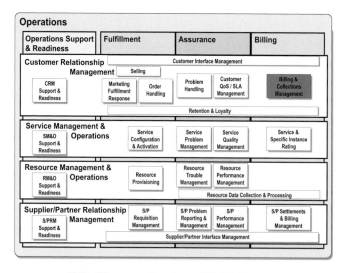

"Billing" Processes – Footprint on eTOM OPS Processes

Process Analysis Tools

The issue of process analysis tools is an important one to address in an assessment. It is important to note that the choice of process analysis tools should come after the organization has gained a solid understanding of the process maturity and their ambitions for process maturity. The tool is what will be used to help the company achieve its goals, rather than the end in itself.

TM Forum does not directly endorse or recommend specific tools, and seeks to make the models and other artifacts that it delivers suitable for use in a wide variety of tool environments. Nevertheless, as there is limited support for a standardized or general method of information interchange with current process analysis tools. In particular, the Casewise Corporate Modeler tool is widely used for the eTOM process model development, particularly within the TM Forum eTOM development team. Other tools such as the Popkin System Architect tool and the Automagic Enterprise Architect tool are also widely used.

For the eTOM work, exchange of the hierarchical process model information is assisted by the use of a common tool, but it is also feasible to transfer this sort of information manually, with some effort in making the transfer. However, as the work in TM Forum is now increasingly focused on eTOM application, including the development of process flows using the eTOM process elements, the complexity of the process information grows, and it becomes less and less attractive to have to translate or re-enter this information manually. Increasingly, therefore, the use of appropriate process modeling tools, either in line with eTOM use or with a capability to automatically import the model data, is indicated.

It should be noted in this context that TM Forum and the eTOM team are considering how to evolve to use of an industry-recognized modeling notation, such as business process management notation (BPMN), and may introduce the use of this notation in future eTOM Releases.

Conclusions from the Process Mapping Exercise

On completion of the process mapping exercise it will be possible to draw conclusions regarding the level of alignment with eTOM in terms of structure and terminology highlighting areas of conflict.

Section 2.3 - Future Process Modeling Opportunities and Strategy

This section should cover the roadmap that the company should follow in simple steps to improve alignment with eTOM and to begin making better use of the eTOM model.

Section 3 – Assessment of Information Architecture

Section 3.1 - Objectives for using the SID

This section of the report is aimed at presenting the results of the assessment of the overall information architecture and how it aligns with the NGOSS SID. It is important at this stage to clearly state the focus (in terms of SID ABEs) for the assessment, as no single assessment is likely to cover the totality of the SID. The focus of the assessment is likely to cover:

• Alignment of the information architecture with the SID

• Definition of a roadmap for use of the SID and opportunities for making use of the SID within the company.

Section 3.2 - Information Architecture Assessment

The assessment of the information architecture should be performed at both a high level and at a detailed entity-by-entity level. The objectives of the assessment should be to identify:

• Areas where there is clear alignment with the SID

• Gaps in the information architecture when compared with the SID

• Areas where the company information architecture is ahead of the SID and might consider feeding some of their internal work back into the industry standard.

High-Level Assessment

When performing the high-level assessment it is important to clearly identify the entities (as defined by the company) that are to be addressed. A typical example of a high-level assessment is shown below.

High Level Information Architecture Assessment

The high-level assessment included the following entities (as defined by the company):

• Subscriber

• Commercial Offering

• Commercial Offering Item

• Commercial Offering Item Cost

• Commercial Offering Order

• Commercial Offering Item Order

• Commercial Offering Item Cost

• Subscriber Commercial Offering

• Service

• Service Cost.

These were compared to the respective SID entities, or groups of entities called Aggregate Business Entities (ABEs).

The **Subscriber** entity embodies a number of SID entities. The SID entities include those within the following ABEs and entities (in parenthesis).

- Party (Party, Individual, Organization, Party Name, Individual Name, Organization Name)

- Party Role (Party Role, Contact Medium [Address], Party Role Association)

- Customer (Customer, Customer Account, Customer Account Bill Cycle)

The **Commercial Offering and Commercial Offering Item** entities are represented by a number of SID entities. The SID entities include those within the following ABEs and entities (in parenthesis)

- Product Specification (Product Specification, Product Specification Type, Product Category)

- Product Offering (Product Offering, Bundled Product Offering, Simple Product Offering)

The **Commercial Offering Item Cost entity** is represented by a number of SID entities. The SID entities include those within the following ABE and entities (in parenthesis)

- Product Offering Price (Product Offering Price, Component Product Offer Price, Prod Offer Price Charge, Recurring Prod Offer Price Charge)

The **Commercial Offering Order, Commercial Offering Item Order, and Commercial Offering Item Cost** entities compare with a number a SID entities. The SID entities include those within the following ABEs and entities (in parenthesis)

- Business Interaction (Business Interaction, Business Interaction Item, Business Interaction Role, Business Interaction Item Price)

• Customer Order (Customer Order, Customer Order Item)

The **Subscriber Commercial Offering, Service, and Service Cost** entities are represented by a number of SID entities. The SID entities include those within the following ABEs and entities (in parenthesis)

• Product (Product, Product Bundle, Product Component, Product Involvement Role, Customer Account Product Involvement, an association to Product Offering Price)

Note: The Service entity is represented in the SID as the Product entity.

Based on this high-level assessment, it was determined that these (System Y) entities embody all of the corresponding SID concepts. While not discussed at the same level of detail as these entities, it was determined that the (System Y) Service entity was comparable to the Service and Service Configuration ABEs.

This high-level assessment gives a first impression of the scope of the company information architecture under consideration and the associated SID ABE's.

Detailed Entity-By-Entity Assessment

Depending on the amount of time available to carry out the assessment, all or a representative sample of the entities should be chosen as the focus of a detailed assessment to determine the overall level of alignment of the information model with the SID.

The detailed assessment involves mapping attributes of information entities to the applicable SID entities' attributes. Upon completion of the mapping a SID conformance level can be ascertained. SID conformance levels are described in the previous chapter. The conformance, or compatibility levels measure the degree to which an entity or group of entities conform to a SID ABE. As such, it measures how well an entity or group of entities is aligned with the respective SID ABE and also measures the effort involved to interoperate with another application for which SID compatibility has been assessed.

The results of this mapping can be represented in a mapping table as shown in the example below. The table contains a column for the information entity's attribute, a column that represents the respective SID entity's attribute, and a third column that contains any applicable comments. An empty cell in the SID attribute column means that there is no corresponding SID attribute. This absence represents a possible new SID attribute or an attribute that represents an application specific extension to the corresponding SID entity. The tables can also be used when constructing application specific extensions to SID XSDs.

Detailed Assessmentof SubsriberEntity

The table below contains the results of mapping the Subscriber entity to the SID Customer ABE.

	Subscriber Mapping	
Subscriber Attribute	**SID Entity/Attribute**	**Comment**
SUBSCRIBER NUMBER	Customer ID and CustomerAccount ID	(COMPANY X) model has one account per customer
INDIVIDUAL NUMBER	IndividualName formOfAddress	INDIVIDUAL NUMBER is the key of a lookup table that contains individual names
SUBSCRIBER TYPE	CustomerAccount accountType	
SUBSCRIBER STATUS	CustomerAccount accountStatus	
SUBSCRIBER FAMILY NAME	IndividualName familiyName	
SUBSCRIBER FIRST NAME	IndividualName givenName	
SUBSCRIBER SECOND NAME	IndividualName middleName	
SUBSCRIBER ADDRESS 1		
SUBSCRIBER ADDRESS 2		
SUBSCRIBER ADDRESS 3		
SUBSCRIBER TOWN	UrbanPropertyAddress municipality	
SUBSCRIBER COUNTY		
SUBSCRIBER POST CODE	UrbanPropertyAddress postcode	
SUBSCRIBER HOME PHONE NUMBER	ContactMedium/TelephoneNumber type and number	

(System Y) Subscriber to SID Customer ABE Mapping Part 1

Subscriber Mapping		
Subscriber Attribute	**SID Entity/Attribute**	**Comment**
SUBSCRIBER WORK PHONE NUMBER	ContactMedium/TelephoneNumber type and number	
SUBSCRIBER FAX NUMBER	ContactMedium/FaxNumber type and number	
SUBSCRIBER EMAIL ADDRESS	ContactMedium/EmailAddress eMailAddress	
SUBSCRIBER MOBILE PAGER NUMBER	ContactMedium/TelephoneNumber type and number	
SUBSCRIBER CREDIT SCORE		
SUBSCRIBER ENTRY DATE		
SUBSCRIBER LAST CHANGED DATE		
SUBSCRIBER RESELLER REFERENCE		Internet customers only; promo code
SUBSCRIBER BILLING DAY	CustomerAccountBillCycle billCycle	
SUBSCRIBER ACTIVATION DATE	PartyRole validFor/startDateTime	
SUBSCRIBER DEACTIVATION DATE	PartyRole validFor/endDateTime	
SUBSCRIBER BILL RESELLER		Flag that indicates not to bill the customer
SUBSCRIBER TEL NUMBER		Not used
RESELLER NUMBER	PartyRoleAssociation associationType and involvesPartyRole	Foreign key to reseller
SUBSCRIBER CREATE SESSION USER		Application name or login of CSR that created the customer

(System Y) Subscriber to SID Customer ABE Mapping Part 2

Based on this detailed assessment, it was determined that the Subscriber entity has attained alignment at SID level 3, with some characteristics of level 4 when assessed against the Customer ABE. Level 3 alignment represents the base level to which an entity should conform.

Features of Note

It is appropriate to call out any special features of note related to the detailed assessment. In the above example it might be appropriate to note that there are two attributes contained within Subscriber that indicate that the information model is somewhat ahead of the SID model's development. SUBSCRIBER CREDIT SCORE (a common attribute kept about customers) and a SUBSCRIBER BILL RESELLER attribute that specifies whether to bill the customer or not, are absent in the SID Customer ABE.

Opportunities for Improved Alignment

It is also appropriate to highlight areas for improved alignment. In the above example it is noted that to further align the model with the SID, Information Architects may want to consider introducing the Party/Party Role concept into the model. This alignment would prove useful if a Party (an individual or organization) can play multiple roles (such as Subscriber or Employee) within the application.

Additionally, information architects may want to pursue parsing the subscriber address into an additional set of attributes that conform to SID postal address attributes, such as street number, street name, and so forth.

Depending on the time and resource available, subsequent detailed mapping tables highlighting features of note and opportunities for improved alignment could then be produced for further Customer Entities as identified in the high level mapping. An overall summary of the entity-by-entity assessment can be produced which forms the basis for the roadmap of future work.

Section 3.3 - Short and Long-Term SID Use Roadmap

Based on the detailed assessment that has gone on before, recommendations can be made regarding using the SID within the target organization. Much of this is covered in Chapter 3 of this book and can be drawn upon to make recommendations to the company as part of the SID use roadmap.

An example of how such a recommendation might look is as follows.

SID as Part of an Application Integration Framework

During a face-to-face meeting with staff it was indicated that the company was considering partnering with another service provider. One facet of the partnership would require interactions between the company's applications and the service provider's application(s). This presents the opportunity for the company to use the SID as part of an integration framework for the interaction between the two applications.

The figure below depicts an example of a partial XML schema that represents company specific extensions to the SID Customer XSD. This XSD is then used to define message payloads for operations that act on Customer Subscriber. The XSD represents a composite of a number of SID entities, including Party Role, Individual Name, Urban Property Address, Contact Medium, Customer, Customer Account, and Customer Account Bill Cycle.

```xml
<xs:complexType name="SIDCustomer">
        <xs:complexContent>
                <xs:restriction base="SIDBusCu:Customer">
                        <xs:sequence>
                                <xs:element name="customerID" type="xs:string"
nillable="true" minOccurs="0"/>
                                <xs:element name="customerStatus" type="xs:string"
nillable="true" minOccurs="0"/>
                        </xs:sequence>
                </xs:restriction>
        </xs:complexContent>
</xs:complexType>
<xs:complexType name="Customer">
        <xs:complexContent>
                <xs:extension base="SystemYSIDBusCu:SIDCustomer">
                        <xs:sequence>
                                <xs:element name="CustomerAccount" type="SystemYSIDBusCu:
CustomerAccount" nillable="true" minOccurs="0"/>
                                <xs:element name="IndividualName" type="SystemYSIDBusCu:
IndividualName" nillable="true" minOccurs="0"/>
                                <xs:element name="UrbanPropertyAddress"
type="SystemYSIDBusCu:UrbanPropertyAddress" nillable="true" minOccurs="0"/>
                                <xs:element name="homePhoneNumber" type="SystemYSIDBusCu:
TelephoneNumber" nillable="true" minOccurs="0"/>
                                <xs:element name="workPhoneNumber" type="SystemYSIDBusCu:
TelephoneNumber" nillable="true" minOccurs="0"/>
                                <xs:element name="faxNumber" type="SystemYSIDBusCu:
FaxNumber" nillable="true" minOccurs="0"/>
                                <xs:element name="emailAddress" type="SystemYSIDBusCu:
EmailContact" nillable="true" minOccurs="0"/>
                                <xs:element name="mobilePagerNumber" type="SystemYSIDBusCu:
TelephoneNumber" nillable="true" minOccurs="0"/>
                                <xs:element name="PartyRole" type="SystemYSIDBusCu:
PartyRole" nillable="true" minOccurs="0"/>
                                <xs:element name="CustomerAccountBillCycle"
type="SystemYSIDBusCu:CustomerAccountBillCycle" nillable="true" minOccurs="0"/>
                                <xs:element name="reNumber" type="SystemYSIDBusCu:
PartyRoleAssociation" nillable="true" minOccurs="0"/>
                                <xs:element name="CustomerExtensions" type="SystemYSIDBusCu:
CustomerExtensions" nillable="true" minOccurs="0"/>
                        </xs:sequence>
                </xs:extension>
        </xs:complexContent>
</xs:complexType>
```

(COMPANY X) Subscriber XSD Fragment

The next figure depicts an XSD that contains the message payload for changing information about a Subscriber used as part of an API to change a Subscriber within (System Y) and/or the partner's application. Note that that customerID attribute has been made mandatory.

```
<xs:complexType name="ChangeSubscriber">
        <xs:complexContent>
                <xs:restriction base="SystemYSIDBusCu:Customer">
                        <xs:sequence>
                                <xs:sequence>
                                        <xs:element name="customerID" type="xs:string"
nillable="false"/>
                                        <xs:element name="customerStatus" type="xs:string"
nillable="true" minOccurs="0"/>
                                </xs:sequence>
                                <xs:element name="CustomerAccount" type="SystemYOpsSIDBusCu:
ChangeSubscriberAccount" nillable="true" minOccurs="0"/>
                                <xs:element name="IndividualName" type="SystemYSIDBusCu:
IndividualName" nillable="true" minOccurs="0"/>
                                <xs:element name="UrbanPropertyAddress"
type="SystemYSIDBusCu:UrbanPropertyAddress" nillable="true" minOccurs="0"/>
                                <xs:element name="homePhoneNumber" type="SystemYSIDBusCu:
TelephoneNumber" nillable="true" minOccurs="0"/>
                                <xs:element name="workPhoneNumber" type="SystemYSIDBusCu:
TelephoneNumber" nillable="true" minOccurs="0"/>
                                <xs:element name="faxNumber" type="SystemYSIDBusCu:
FaxNumber" nillable="true" minOccurs="0"/>
                                <xs:element name="emailAddress" type="SystemYSIDBusCu:
EmailContact" nillable="true" minOccurs="0"/>
                                <xs:element name="mobilePagerNumber" type="SystemYSIDBusCu:
TelephoneNumber" nillable="true" minOccurs="0"/>
                                <xs:element name="PartyRole" type="SystemYSIDBusCu:
PartyRole" nillable="true" minOccurs="0"/>
                                <xs:element name="CustomerAccountBillCycle"
type="SystemYSIDBusCu:CustomerAccountBillCycle" nillable="true" minOccurs="0"/>
                                <xs:element name="reNumber" type="SystemYSIDBusCu:
PartyRoleAssociation" nillable="true" minOccurs="0"/>
                                <xs:element name="CustomerExtensions" type="SystemYSIDBusCu:
CustomerExtensions" nillable="true" minOccurs="0"/>
                        </xs:sequence>
                </xs:restriction>
        </xs:complexContent>
</xs:complexType>
```

Change Subscriber XSD Fragment

The assessment team may choose to include or embed a complete sample of XSDs in the report from which the fragments were extracted along with a sample XML documents.

A longer-term objective would be to develop an application integration framework based on the SID that would be used to integrate internal company applications. For example, interactions with the company's Inventory Management Application (IMA) could employ SID XML schema-based APIs to loosen the coupling between the applications. The loosened coupling would be the result of shielding the APIs from internal database schema changes within the application.

Section 4 – Review of the Implementation Architecture relative to the TNA

Section 4.1 - Objectives of the implementation Architecture Assessment

This section of the report is aimed at presenting the results of the assessment of the overall implementation architecture and how it aligns with the NGOSS Technology-Neutral Architecture principles (TNA). The focus of the assessment is likely to cover:

- Alignment of the implementation architecture approach with the NGOSS TNA

- Definition of a roadmap for improved alignment with the TNA.

Section 4.2 - Implementation Architecture Evaluation

Introduction
As a first step in any assessment it is important to clearly identify the current state of the implementation architecture based on company documentation and discussions/interviews with key personnel. It is also important to define the scope of the investigation regarding which systems/applications are to be assessed and which aspects are going to be covered in the assessment.

For example, the assessment may decide to cover only applications A, B & C within the company and only from the perspective of security, policy, integration and workflow. The assessment team may specifically decide to exclude assessments of implementation methodology, use of use-cases, and so forth, depending on the time and expertise available to the assessment team.

An example summary of a current state assessment is shown below.

Applications Summary

Many of the applications in the company solution are legacy systems built to specification (both in-house and by external providers). The following table shows the target company applications, the nature of each application (package / legacy) and other high level information about the applications.

Application Name	COTS or Internal	Main Technology	Integration Methods	Workflow Approach	Security/policy Management Approach	Comments (e.g. scalability & performance)
Generic X	Internal	Java, .NET, ASP, .COM (??), SQL Server	SOAP over HTTP, link to ASP, MSMQ	Within application	Active Directory	XML builds to 0.5Mb per session. Load is spread across portal servers.
Generic Y	Internal	Java, .NET, ASP, .COM (??), SQL Server	SOAP over HTTP, link to ASP, MSMQ	Within application	Active Directory	
Fault Z (Fault Management)	Internal	SQL Server, ASP, .COM	COM+, linked ASP	Within application	Active Directory	
Banner	Customized OPAL	As per OPAL	As per APOL	Within Application	Active Directory	As per ONYX
LOCK	Internal	SQL Server, .NET, IIS, SQL Server	SOAP over HTTP, CD for new addresses	Within application	Active Directory	
ReturnView	Package (customized)	Solaris, Oracle, stored procedures	Oracle calls, FTP	Within application	By application	Scalability and flexibility uncertain.
Rate	Package	Oracle	FTP	Within application	By application	

Biller	Internal		MSMQ	Within application	By application	Concerns about performance and scalability. Operational window is a constraint. Billing is performed every day which can complicate catch-up (when required). A database Index re-build required regularly, this improves performance by ½ hour.
Record	Internal	SQL Server	FTP	Within application	By application	
Provision	Various	Various	Internal messaging	Within application	By application	
Inventory	Internal	Solaris, Oracle	WebLogic, J2EE, SOAP	From Orchestrator	Active Directory	
WorkForce	Package	Solaris, Oracle	XMLRPC	Within application	By application	

This table should also be backed up with additional relevant detail on each of the application areas and any additional observations that may be made that impact on the flexibility, reliability or usability of the systems. Some examples of additional comments are shown below.

Legacy data conversion issues

As a result of legacy data and because of conversion issues the linking and merging of customer data is poor. In some cases customers have three records disassociated from each other.

Performance and scalability

Performance and scalability issues are addressed to some extent in the above table. There are general concerns about the performance and scalability of some parts of the solution. The main issue, currently, is the operational window for end-of-day routines (billing and so forth) is extremely tight, there is a short window and billing runs every day. Consequently, billing overruns or missed bill runs have a knock-on effect into subsequent operational windows

Historically performance testing has not been a reliable predictor of the production system. Typically the first indications of performance issues (for example, after software upgrade or converted data) were within the initial production run. There are efforts underway to address this situation and make performance testing more representative of production.

As a rough estimate, staff stated that there is currently a 50-60% load on system, however there is considerably more data to be converted onto the system.

The company in general, is using a significant number of Microsoft based servers and software. In some cases there have been issues with performance and throughput. A new 64 bit SQL server is currently under test to asses its ability to improve performance.

System upgrades

Software migration for a major release requires a considerable amount of planning, effort and system downtime. Major releases are implemented in a direct cutover. As an example, the recent release required six days downtime for implementation (as planned). This implementation did not include a data conversion component.

While there is some level of patch release, this process is not yet mature. Change requests implemented outside major releases need a lot of effort to be implemented and are generally avoided.

The migration is complicated due to the architecture of the solution and the technologies employed.

Section 4.3 - Analysis of Implementation Architecture Relative to NGOSS TNA Approach

This section assesses the current architecture against the NGOSS TNA principles and policies. The NGOSS principles relevant for this assessment are that:

• Solutions have separate business process flow

• Solutions have re-usable components

• Component have clearly defined contract interfaces

• Solutions have a common communications mechanism

• Solutions are implemented as loosely coupled, distributed systems.

An example of some comments from an assessment are shown below.

Separation of business process flow from components

Overview of Principle

An NGOSS system must separate the operation of the components from the software that orchestrates the business process across these components. That is, there should be no hard coding of business rules within the solution applications. This enables:

• Re-use of business processes

• Multi-level business processes

• Improved flexibility

• A common view of the business processes.

Analysis

Many of the applications have the business processes embedded within the individual applications. In particular, the X and Y applications have a heavily embedded workflow with the application controlling both the user and system interfaces.

This is an infringement of the NGOSS TNA principles and can lead to the following disadvantages:

- Fragmented and difficult to maintain business processes

- Difficulty in re-use of business processes

- Maintenance overhead in business process support

- Difficulties in the integration of and re-use of components.

The orchestrator is used effectively as an orchestration tool for some of the integration between the applications and generally supports the NGOSS TNA policies. This effectively controls the interaction between external systems handling results (both positive and negative) in a predictable and repeatable manner. This is not to say that the orchestrator is suitable as the overall orchestration tool (it may or may not), merely that it exhibits some of the behaviors absent in other areas of the solution.

The situation is aggravated by the fact that some of the processes for "business customers" are controlled manually (in other words, relies on the user to know what to do next).

Conclusion

With fragmented business processes embedded into the applications, significant effort will be required to maintain and develop these processes (as opposed to centrally defining the business processes). Additionally, there are demonstrable benefits to removing the business process logic from the portals and providing a mechanism that will allow several components to share the same business process logic (that is, use other interfaces with the same results and a common process layer).

Recommendation 1:
The company should investigate, identify, select and implement a suitable orchestration tool to be used for business process definition and the control of components using these business processes. The tool should support the NGOSS TNA principles and policies if it is to assist in the delivery of an NGOSS architecture.

Recommendation 2:
Implementation of the orchestration tool should be performed on a phased basis, with consideration for developing and area or areas with a significant support cost. That is, the tool should be used to obtain the largest benefits in the shortest timeframe.

Recommendation 3:
Business justification for the tool must be based on the lifetime value of the tool rather than the initial implementation. Special consideration must be given to the savings and opportunities presented by a centrally defined and controlled business process.

Recommendation 4:
The tool must support the volumes of transaction required by the business and in particular must be scalable to cater for increasing volumes. The tool should have a proven record of catering for similar volumes with suitable performance.

Recommendation 5:

Selection of the tool may be considered with the implementation of recommendation 6 below.

Integration Aspects

Overview of Principle

An NGOSS solution depends on services to support the operation of the architecture and mechanisms to provide inter working between the components. These are defined within NGOSS as:

• Framework services

• OSS framework services

• Basic framework services

• Basic mechanisms

• Common communication mechanism

• Invocation mechanism.

The manifestation of this is in (NGOSS) applications having well defined and documented interfaces and the overall integration supported through tools such as a messaging bus.

Analysis and Recommendations.

There are a significant number and diversity of integration and messaging methods within the solution. The absence of a common communication mechanism not only complicates the architecture, but promotes discrepancies in the policies, principles and standards across the integration.

Recommendation 6.

It is strongly recommended to rationalize the communication mechanism across the (System Y) solution. It is essential that these efforts are attentive to the other services and mechanisms required within as part of the NGOSS architecture as these may be satisfied within a common tool.

Also due to the nature of the implementation of the solution there is incomplete documentation of the contracts. This inhibits capabilities of the solution as well as increasing the support and development costs for several reasons:

- Skilled resources are needed to discover the definitions

- This process is time consuming and does not take advantage of previous efforts

- This method of contract definition is error-prone and can easily miss esoteric elements (such as behavior characteristics).

Recommendation 7.

Contracts within the solution should be defined using the NGOSS TMF053B template. This will ensure that all the characteristics of the interface definition are uniformly documented and captured.

From a practical point of view, the initial thrust of this may be focused on contracts impacted by new developments, with progressively more contracts being defined throughout the subsequent projects. Additionally this documentation exercise may become part of a maintenance process where the documentation is produced as part of the support function.

To achieve the overall benefit of an NGOSS architecture, total documentation of the interfaces is essential and a plan must exist to achieve this in a reasonable timescale.

It should be remembered that the principles and policies of NGOSS are independent of the technologies employed and are intended to provide guidelines for best practice and are not overly proscriptive. It must also be emphasized that this review should be a critique of how the current implementation meets these policies and standards, not of the actual technologies themselves.

Appendix

Abbreviations and References

Abbreviations

ABE	Aggregate Business Entity
API	Application Program Interface
ATM	Asynchronous Transfer Method
BPMN	Business Process Management Notation
BSS	Business Support Systems
CBE	Core Business Entity
COTS	Commercial Off The Shelf Software
CRM	Customer Relationship Management
eTOM	Enhanced Telecommunications Operations Map
FAB	Fulfillment, Assurance, Billing
IP	Internet Protocol
ISV	Independent Software Vendor
IT	Information Technology
ITU-T	International Telecommunications Union – Telecoms Division
M&OM	Marketing & Offer Management
MDA	Model Driven Architecture
NGOSS	New Generation OSS
NGOSS TNA	NGOSS Technology Neutral Architecture
OS&R	Operations Support & Readiness
RACI	Responsible, Accountable, Consult, Inform
RD&M	Resource Development & Management
RM&O	Resource Management & Operations
RUP	Rational Unified Process
SANRR	Scope, Analyze, Normalize, Rationalize, Rectify

SCD&M	Supply Chain Development & Management
SDH	Synchronous Digital Hierarchy
SD&M	Service Development & Management
SID	Shared Information and Data model
SIP	Strategy, Infrastructure, Product
SM&O	Service Management & Operations
SONET	Synchronous Optical NETwork
SQL	Structured Query Language
SRM	Supplier/Partner Relationship Management
TCO	Total Cost of Ownership
UML	United Modeling Language
TMF	TeleManagement Forum
XML	eXtensible Markup Language
XSD	XML schema definition

NGOSS 5.0 Release

The latest NGOSS release at the time of going to print with this book is NGOSS Release 5.0. This is made up of a large number of documents covering all the areas set out in this book.

DOCUMENT NUMBER	DOCUMENT NAME
Lifecycle	
GB927	NGOSS Lifecycle & Methodology
eTOM	
GB921	eTOM Main Document
GB921B	eTOM – B2B Integration: Using B2B Inter-enterprise integration with the eTOM
GB921C	Public B2B Business Operations Map Application Note
GB921D	Process Decompositions & Descriptions
GB921F	Process Flow Examples
GB921N	eTOM – NGOSS Contract Examples
GB921P	eTOM Primer
GB921T	eTOM – M.3400 Mapping Application Note
GB921V	eTOM – An Interim View of an Interpreter's Guide for eTOM and ITIL Practitioners
SID	
GB922	SID Business View: Concepts & Principles
GB922 – 0	Primer for the SID Business View
GB922 – 1A	SID Agreement
GB922 – 1BI	SID Business Interaction
GB922 – 1BT	SID Business Entity Base Types
GB922 – 1C	SID Business Contract
GB922 – 1J	SID Project
GB922 – 1L	SID Location
GB922 – 1P	SID Party
GB922 – 1POL	SID Policy
GB922 – 1R	SID Root Business Entities
GB922 – 1T	SID Time Related Entities
GB922 – 1U	Using the SID (UML models)
GB922 – 2	SID Customer
GB922 – 3	SID Produc
GB922 – 4S-O	SID Service Overview
GB922 – 4S-QoS	SID Quality of Service
GB922 – 5LR	SID Logical Resource
GB922 – 5PR	SID Physical Resource
GB926	SID System View: Concepts & Principles

DOCUMENT NUMBER	DOCUMENT NAME
Service Framework	
GB924	Service Framework Guidebook
Architecture	
TMF053	Technology Neutral Architecture
TMF053B	TNA: Business & System View Contract
TMF053C	TNA: Behavior & Control Services
TMF053D	TNA: Metamodel
TMF053F	TNA: Framework Services
TMF053S	TNA: Security Addendum
Compliance	
TMF050	NGOSS Compliance Testing Strategy Technical Specification
TMF050A	NGOSS Compliance Testing Information Model & Testing Rules
Application Map	
GB929	Telecoms Applications Map – The OSS Systems Landscape
CIM/SID	
GB932	DMTF/TMF Model Alignment - Physical Sub-model
GB933	DMTF/TMF Model Alignment - SID Logical Resources and CIM Networks Sub-models
General	
TMF044	Glossary of Terms
TMF052	NGOSS Requirements Document

Other References and Suggested Reading

Open Distributed Processing Reference Model: Overview, 1998, International Organization for Standardization, ISO/IEC 10746-1.

Ivar Jacobson, Grady Booch, James Rumbaugh, **The Unified Software Development Process, 1999**, Addison-Wesley, ISBN 0-2011-57169-2.

Joaquin Miller & Jishnu Mukerji, **MDA Guide Version 1.0.1,** June 2003, Object Management Group, OMG/2003-06-01.

Michael Porter, Competitive Advantage: **Creating & Sustaining Superior Performance**, 1998, Free Press; 1st Free Press Edition, ISBN 068481460.

John A. Zachman, **A Framework for Information Systems Architecture**, IBN Systems Journal, vol 26, no 3, 1987, IBM Publication G321-5298.

Index

A

ABE: *See Aggregate Business Entity*

B

business entity, 104-110, 121, 135, 159, 162

business flow, 172

business goal, 28-29

business logic, 115, 166

business object, 19, 120-130

business objective, 19

business process, 21-22, 27-28, 31, 33-36, 47

business requirement, 19, 28, 33-35, 87, 89, 150

business use case, 29

business view, 23, 24-30, 47

business view contract, 59, 64, 114, 137

business view model, 47, 55, 132

C

Casewise Corporate Modeler, 177

change management, 144

class, 14, 45, 47, 53, 55, 106, 125, 131

class diagram, 53, 131

Common Business Entities, 101

common communication mechanism, 196

common framework, 22, 34

common information model, 14, 19

compatibility table, 163

compliance, 95, 110-111, 145, 157, 161

compliance criteria, 110-111

compliance program, 95, 157

Compliance team, 161

component, 20-21, 25, 30, 42, 56-59, 65-67

component implementation, 56, 73, 115, 137, 140, 142, 165-166

conformance, 95, 96, 110, 111, 137, 144-147, 156, 161, 162

conformance criteria, 145, 157, 161-162

conformance level, 182

container, 23, 148

contract, 20-24, 28-31, 33, 35,

D

E

F

G

H

I

implementation, 20-24, 27-33

implementation engineer review, 154

implementation view, 8, 9, 11, 26, 28-30, 55, 65-66, 75, 125-126, 132-133, 142

implementer, 76, 95, 113-114

independent software vendor, 4, 18, 22, 74, 111, 119, 148

industry standard, 33, 35, 71, 74, 76, 101, 127, 178

information architect, 162, 185

information architecture, 6, 21, 178-179, 181

information framework, 13-14, 19, 48

information model, 9, 14, 18-19, 23, 33, 44, 72,95,109,147,149,157,160-161,182,185

information technology, 32

information-orientated, 33, 133

integration, 12-14, 19-20, 32-34, 72-74, 95-96, 110, 130, 135-142, 157-158, 164, 186, 189-196

interacting, 110, 162

interaction, 6-11, 20-21, 28-29, 40-46, 55, 59, 62-65, 73, 82-83, 86, 112, 114, 148, 149, 150, 174, 180, 186, 189, 194

interaction architecture, 6-7, 21, 29, 45, 55, 59, 62, 65, 71, 73, 112, 137

interaction diagram, 83, 114

interaction point, 65, 114

interface, 12, 24, 56, 59, 65-67, 71-12, 81-93, 113

interface definition, 113, 197,

interoperability, 9, 19-23, 29, 56, 64, 96, 101, 110-113, 168

interoperability tax, 20

inoperate, 23, 58, 149, 164, 182

interoperating database, 117

interview, 153-154

invocation mechanism, 196

ISV, 74, 111

interactive, 15, 18, 22, 24, 59, 124

ITU-T, 1-12, 15, 17, 26, 28, 70

K

L

M

N

O

object, 42, 44, 64, 112, 121, 123, 142
object classes, 142
object-orientated, 112
operational requirement, 116
Operational Support System, 116
operations, 42, 48-49, 53, 58, 66-67, 77, 87, 92-93, 128, 136, 152, 171, 173, 186
Operations Systems and Software, 12, 17
organizational maturity, 78
OSS: 12, 14, 22, 41, 55-56, 116, 135, 196
OSS through Java™ Initiative, 22, 55, 142

P

pattern, 107-108
perspective, 27, 42, 47, 50, 58, 75, 90, 96-97, 111, 114, 126, 158, 172, 190, 195
physical, 10-11, 25-28, 58, 67, 75-76, 126, 142, 152, 190
physical perspective, 27-28, 75-76, 126
physical view, 25, 152
policy management, 58, 190
policy-enabled, 19, 56-57, 118, 165-167, 190
policy-enabled architecture, 56-57, 115, 165-167
policy-managed, 116
post-condition, 58, 65, 114
pre- and post-condition, 65, 114
pre-condition, 58
primary eTOM level 2 Process, 50, 61
process architect, 6-7, 21, 65, 79, 152-155, 171-172
process architecture, 6-7, 21, 65, 152, 155, 171-172
process automation, 3, 5, 33
process aware, 77-78, 153, 171
process centric, 78, 153, 171
process decomposition, 44

Q

R

S

T

U

UML 14, 19, 47, 50, 52-53, 95, 157, 159
UML class diagram, 53
UML model, 50, 52, 53, 95, 157, 159
Unified Modeling Language, 19
Unified Software Development Process, 23-24
Use case diagram, 40, 44, 144, 130, 132, 134, 138
use case realization, 139
use case template, 138
user interface, 2, 9-12, 87, 125-126, 140, 164
user-defined rules, 116

V

vendor, 4, 14, 18, 22, 30, 35, 74, 111, 119-120, 148, 163
viewpoint, 22-23
visibility, 19, 20, 23, 149, 174

W

W3C.org, 99
workflow, 8, 190, 194

X

XML, 47, 95-96, 99-100, 110, 135-136, 142, 157-159, 164, 186, 189-190
XML schema, 47, 95-96, 135-136, 142, 157-159, 164, 186, 189
XSD, 96-98, 100, 186-188

Z

Zachman Framework, 23, 24